LORDS OF THE KNOWN WORLDS

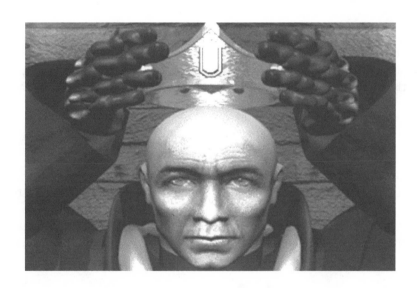

by
Bill Bridges, Jackie Cassada, Sam Chupp,
James Estes, Andrew Greenberg,
Rustin Quaide, Nicky Rea

Credits

Written by: Bill Bridges, Jackie Cassada, Sam Chupp, James Estes, Andrew Greenberg, Rustin Quaide, Nicky Rea

Additional material on House al-Malik: Phil Brucato and Samuel Inabinet

Developed and typeset by: Bill Bridges

Edited by: Jennifer Hartshorn

Art directed by: John Bridges

Art by: John Bridges, Mark Jackson, Brian LeBlanc, Larry MacDougall, John Poreda, Alex Sheikman, Ron Spencer

Title page art by: Rival Productions (for the *Emperor of the Fading Suns* computer game)

Cover art by: Michael William Kaluta

Emblem:

The strips along the spine (front and back cover) display the emblems of the minor houses detailed in this book. They are: (front cover) Juandaastas, Justinian, Keddah, Masseri, Shelit, Thana; (back cover) Torenson, Trusnikron, Van Gelder, Xanthippes. Following these are the emblems of: Ur-Obun Council, Ur-Ukar Chiefdom, and Vorox Kingdom.

Pilgrims:

Would'st thou become kings among men? Look to your breeding first! The Pancreator has wisely seperated the escola seeds from the husks, the pure from the base. Look instead to your fields, to your own harvests, that you might better reap the bounty of your own souls. Nay, sully not yourselves with the ways of man and power. Such a curse is not for you, happy in your ignorance. Let the cursed bear such burdens and reap as their rewards the wealth of the world. You humble have the wealth of the Empyrean coming to you. And yet still you envy those condemned to their worldly palaces, prisons of the soul.

Holistic Design Inc.
5002-H N. Royal Atlanta Dr.
Tucker, GA 30084

Visit Holistic Design's web site at:

www.holistic-design.com

Printed in the US of A

LORDS OF THE KNOWN WORLDS

Contents

Alustro's Journal: On Meeting a Noble

Nobles are most perplexing. My time in Lady Erian Li Halan's service has taught me that, but offered little insight otherwise. I have not the upbringing to fathom their thoughts, and thus their deeds remain largely unpredictable to me. I live by the guidelines of the Prophet, with compassion before all. They have other... priorities. I say this not to diminish them. How can one such as I, a novitiate in a small and ill-famed order, through word or deed ever tarnish those of noble blood? If, as some say, they were born to their high peak by the Pancreator's will, then the words of those below them can mean little, even those words blessed to reach them past the furious winds which blow at such heights.

No, I in no way infer a political statement behind my musings. I simply wonder at times. If but a few nobles could put aside their obsessive duties and place the well being of their charges first in their hearts, then perhaps the darkness which devours the suns would not seem so cold to those who suffer in its dimming light.

Perhaps I had best give example before my confusing thoughts yield heresy.

I had returned with Erian and her entourage to Vera Cruz after our harrowing expedition to the barbarian world of Kurga, of which I will say no more here. We were forced to abandon our starship for fear that it would lead the Inquisitors to us. We set out on beastback to hide ourselves in the remote mountains for a time, hoping the Inquisitors would turn their hunt to another world, figuring we had moved on. With minimal supplies, we left the last settlement listed on our maps and went to the wilderness.

We soon found that the maps were wrong. Drawn up and made available by noble decree, they omitted what the nobility hid in shame.

Two days into our journey, with no sign of any village or even a manor house, we came upon a field of peasant workers. I know they saw us, but they nonetheless pretended they had not. We could hear a commotion up the road, concealed around a bend. By the furtive glances the peasants gave this area, I knew it was the source of their fear.

We rounded the corner and saw a cruel scene. A man was on the ground, writhing in the mud and grunting in pain, suffering the terrible lashes of a whip, which was thrashed wildly by a stripling in noble garb.

I acted without thinking and only later realized how foolish it was. My compassion got the better of me, but I endangered my Lady with it. Without even considering that the victim of such torture might be a criminal who deserved this treatment, I jumped off my horse and ran to him. I grasped the long tail of the whip as it was drawn back before it could strike again, and yelled in anger at the startled boy who held it.

His eyes widened in shock but he quickly recovered, snarled at me, and sent me reeling with a backhand. I flopped into the mud alongside the whipping victim, and immediately felt the lash myself. Oh, I will never understand how the man beside me withstood 10 lashings let alone one without crying like a babe from the sheer pain of it. I could not withstand the one lash, and did cry out.

There did not come another. When I opened my teary eyes, the noble boy was lying in the mud before me, unhorsed himself. Beyond him stood Erian, sword drawn.

"Get up, boy," she said. "If you would dare to strike a member of my entourage — a priest, for Prophet's sake — then you would surely be bold enough to settle the matter properly. Draw your blade!"

The boy scowled at her with a most ugly expression. Indeed, he looked the most ill-bred of any noble I have yet seen. But he certainly had reflexes, for he was up with sword drawn in a second, with his steel aimed straight for Erian's throat.

She casually tapped the thrust aside and flicked her blade at his wrist, drawing a thin line of blood. He scowled deepened, if it can be imagined, and began a hail of blows, all easily parried by my Lady.

I looked to Cardanzo, Erian's bodyguard, who had not even dismounted. He sat on his horse smirking. I knew

Erian was in no danger. Few men can size up an opponent as quickly as Cardanzo, and if he saw no danger for our Lady, then there was none.

I picked myself up and bent down to attend to the poor wretch I had attempted to save from misery. The clang of swords continued behind me as I examined the man. The lashes had cut deep in some areas, now splattered with mud. He would need washing and a bed to properly heal.

I turned to watch the duel in time to see it end. Erian, finally tired of toying with the boy, disarmed him and sent his blade flying into the field. A few peasants ran from the spot at which it landed, afraid to be near it. The boy was panting and exhausted, but his anger seethed from him, hot enough to warm a small hut on a cold winter's night.

"Admit your defeat, boy," Erian said. "Or fetch your blade for more."

The boy growled and ran to his sword. He was soon back, hacking furiously at Erian, who was actually surprised and somewhat angry now herself.

Anger is the great undoer. He pushes us to precipices we would rather not fall from.

Erian struck out and sliced the boy's forearm, not enough to cripple, but enough to end his days as a duelist for a long time. As he fell to the ground screaming and clutching his wounded arm, horse's hooves sounded loudly on the road ahead. In moments, a horse rounded the bend and stopped short, kicking mud up into the air.

A wild, blacktressed demoness leapt from the mount and marched toward the boy. Never have I seen such an impressive lady or such a seething anger. But I could not tell at whom it was directed — the boy or us?

She said nothing but I could tell by the way the boy's eyes beseeched her that she was his mother. She looked at the wound in contempt and then turned her attention to Erian.

"You have wounded my son, lady," she said. "Are you prepared to stand trial for restitution?"

"I'll do no such thing," Erian cried. "I had just right to challenge your boy. You'd know that for sure, but then, you're the one who raised him to strike priests!"

"I raised him no such way!" the lady yelled. "Defend your actions then!" She drew sword and waited for Erian.

I could not believe this. I had thought the matter swiftly ended, but here was yet another noble seeking yet another duel. And Erian, without a moment's hesitation, gave it to her.

Their swords flashed in the light of the coming sunset as they paced about each other, each seeking the other's measure. I looked to Cardanzo to see that he had left his mount and now watched the battle intently. By the way his eyes never wavered from the blades, I knew that Erian had perhaps met her match. All because I had foolishly acted, creating a chain of events which inevitably led to this, vendetta upon vendetta.

Fear gripped my heart, for I knew that my Lady's energy shield was inoperative, for our fusion batteries had long since run out. I could not allow this! I cried out: "Hold your sword! My lady is at a disadvantage — I can see that you have an energy shield while she does not!"

"Still your tongue, Alustro!" Erian yelled.

But her opponent stepped back and dropped her blade. "Good priest, I thank you. I would not have it be said that my accouterments won a battle rather than my hand. I remove my shield." She unhooked an elaborate brooch which she wore on her cloak, and placed it in her saddlebags. "Now, have at you!" she yelled and engaged Erian.

I prayed for my Lady, using no theurgy or rite which was unseemly to a duel, but with the simple means of faith instead. If she was in the right, surely the Pancreator would grant her victory. I winced as the first full strike hit steel, sending a clang echoing across the field. The peasants had all stopped their work and were staring gape-jawed at the fight.

Swords moved so swiftly I could not mark the battle. Parry became riposte, becoming feint and then slash, punctuated by moments of supernal stillness, then broken once again by flashing blades. Both combatants were nicked and bloody, but with no major wounds on either side.

But as the sun moved closer to the horizon and the sky grew red, the mysterious lady's face grew softer, and her grim expression slowly became a smile, which rose to her eyes. Then, she drew back and raised her sword for truce.

"You fight well, lady," she said. "We are both tired and have not yet got the full measure of the other. What say we call a truce and end this duel?"

"I accept your terms," Erian, panting, replied. "You fight most well indeed. It would seem we are both the match for the other. I doubt that even another hour of dueling would decide the outcome."

The swordswoman laughed. "True. True, indeed. It is rare to meet such an accomplished and honorable noble in these parts. Would you return with me to my manor and be my guest? I am most curious about you now, and would be offended were you to refuse."

How odd! She had wanted to soundly thrash my lady moments before. Now, her rage was turned to... affection? The offer seemed to be most genuine, with no hint of guile behind it, and I am glad my Lady accepted it, for we had as yet no place to stay for the night.

But our host's boy was not happy about the offer. He scowled at his mother, climbed on his mount, and rode off down the road. I was surprised to see that she cared little about his actions, even rolling her eyes as if to suggest to us that the boy was overly dramatic in his actions. Most perplexing, indeed.

The manor was but a mile up the road. Not the richest lodging we had seen, but it was most comfortable. The lady had even graciously helped me to place the wounded peasant on my mount and offered her chuirgeon to aid him. Thus, I joined our entourage at supper a bit late, as I took it upon myself to ensure that the wounded man was put to bed well. As I entered the dining room, I was greeted with laughter and joy. Our hostess was listening to some of Erian's tales of our lighter adventures, and she seemed fully caught up in the humor of them. A most remarkable change from earlier.

"Ah, Alustro," Erian said as I sat down, "Is all well with your charge?"

"Yes, my Lady," I replied. "He will do fine. His wounds will heal aright." Our host's face darkened somewhat as I said this, not out of anger, but shame.

"Our gracious host, Baroness Shariza Hazat de Laguna, has explained the incident to us," Erian said.

"But I owe an explanation to the priest, also," the baroness said. "My son learned only the ways of cruelty from my husband. He knows not how to treat the serfs in a manner befitting the Pancreator's creations. Had you not already intervened, and had it not been a matter of family honor to defend him before strangers, I would have lashed him with his own whip. Of all the misery my dishonored husband left me, he is the worst."

"I... I am sorry, baroness," I stammered.

"Why? It is not your doing. No, my husband chose to betray his liege during the wars, and in return his widow is given only the least of his manors on the least — and now last — of his lands, a prisoner far from society where she can no longer harm his reputation."

It seemed to me that her exile perhaps had less to do with her husband than with her own outspoken manner. She seemed a great lady, but in the fashion of many nobles, greatness leads to great enemies. Indeed, as the night went on, we talked long about our exploits and listened intently to hers. She and Erian had built a bond of sorts on the field which only grew tighter as time passed. They had so much in common, both wronged by their royal connections.

We stayed at the Baroness Shariza Hazat de Laguna's manor for a week. During that time, Erian cemented a friendship it seems will last a lifetime. Rarely were those two apart, talking always about noble affairs and how to overturn their bad fortunes. By the end of our stay, we knew we had an ally for whenever we needed it. I don't think Erian wanted to leave when we did, for the baroness was the first compatriot she had meet since her exile. But the vision afforded by the Gargoyle of Nowhere drove us on.

The whole affair was most perplexing, even if it did have good outcome. How can the shattering sound of steel upon steel lead to such a true friendship? Most people make their friends in more civil ways, but it seems that nobles must first ascertain the power of another before they can be unguarded before them. Is this any basis for true human companionship?

Perhaps its the truest and most enduring basis. I hope not. It would be a crueler world than I imagine if all human interaction was reduced to hierarchies of power. But then again, there is surely evil out to thwart all good people. Perhaps only in the heat of such passion, tested where there is little chance for guile, can we truly come to know another.

Introduction: The Noble Estate

It is said that there are four "estates" of power within the Known Worlds: the nobility, the Universal Church, the Merchant League, and the Emperor. Of these, the most ubiquitous, resourceful, enduring and cunning is that of the nobility. Like it or not, nobles hold the reins of power, for even the Emperor comes from their ranks and may one day be deposed by them.

Their own press speaks highly of their magnanimity, but their detractors constantly grumble about oppression and revolt. The topic of royal reform is an ongoing debate in the Known Worlds. Most believe that reform can only come from within — from the nobles themselves. To overthrow the nobles from the outside (from the people) may not end the estate in the future, so tenacious has it proven in the past. The Second Republic failed to abolish the institution — nobles remained through guile and popularity. Stripped of actual power, they remained as symbols, appreciated and sometimes adored by the populace much like British royalty or the American Kennedy family in the late 20th century.

Indeed, there seems to be a need in the human psyche for a "family of families." But is this an innate characteristic or simply a historical accident? What is the nature of noble power and endurance? Can the many actually rule the many, or does it eventually come down to a few ruling over all?

Many claim that humanity is too disparate to be ruled by democratic interests, labeled as the rule of mediocrity by critics. Perhaps the unity provided by blood — the undeniable physical fact, represented by the symbol of the royal family — is required to bring humans together. Even if a revolutionary gains political power, can he successfully relinquish it to the people without a concurrent societal revolution as well? Until humans get nobles out of their psyches, the lords won't leave their towers. Power seems to coalesce into oligarchies and cabals.

The estate of the nobility, when considered galactically, is an oligarchy — rule by a few, made up of local dictatorships. The estate of the Emperor, however, radically changes this concept, putting one person over all. The regent was a mere puppet, an empty symbol — but an actual Emperor is something that resonates in the depths of consciousness, reaching to the very roots of our concepts of power and leadership.

Even the Church has borrowed noble forms of rule, as has the League. But there is more room for meritocracy in both of these factions, for among the nobility, merit-based promotion is rarely extended outside the bloodline.

Regardless of debate, the nobles of the Known Worlds are a reality, and characters must deal with them — whether because they themselves are noble, are members of a noble entourage, or are themselves oppressed by their noble lords.

How to Become a Noble

The most obvious method of joining the noble estate is to be born into it. Blood privilege goes farther than any other method — indeed, it is practically the only method. The granting of knighthoods is rare enough that the infusion of new blood does little to bring down class standards. The risk of bringing an uncouth, ill-bred knight into the ranks of rulership is thankfully small.

Knighthoods are usually granted only to freemen, but in dire circumstances a serf may be the recipient of noble largess. The Emperor Wars saw many such battlefield promotions granted by nobles desperate to bolster loyalty in the face of desertion or mutiny. Safe in the assumption that the new knight could then usually be assigned to a suicide mission, this became a tactical maneuver by many disliked nobles. To their patron's shame, some of these new serf-lords survived the wars and now proudly display their noble status at upperclass soirees.

The Privileges of Rank

While there are the divisions of major and minor house (the five major houses are called the Royal Houses), there are also essentially two types of nobles: landed and non-landed. The non-landed are practically second-class citizens among high society. They may hold title and even wealth, but with land comes prestige (and the stability to maintain it for generations).

Most lords inherit their lands, but it is possible to gain them through merit (or cunning) from another lord. A land grant is either hereditary (handed down to the recipient's heirs) or for one lifetime only (the grantor regains ownership upon the death of the recipient). Obviously, the former is the more desired form, for without hereditary land, a lord is often considered transitory to other nobles.

Hereditary grants are rare, however, for few lords wish to part forever with lands which may be desperately needed in later years for income or resources. They are awarded sparsely and most often simply to keep the institution alive, to appease the young nobles and give them the figment of mobility.

Lands may be lost through war or misfortune. For instance, the head of the family can seize lands as punishment from a prosecuted noble. Some lords rack up large enough debts so that their collected taxes go immediately toward paying their debtors, leaving themselves destitute. After the Emperor Wars, it is not uncommon to see a landless and poor count. Indeed, the turmoil and chaos of the Emperor Wars have left many nobles adrift. Many thus adventure to reclaim lost revenue, to relieve debt or to stave off boredom.

Noble Benefices and Afflictions

Below are some new Benefices and Afflictions available to noble characters. Details pertaining a character's particular house or circumstance should be worked out between player and gamemaster.

Background

Benefices

Famous Ancestor (1-4 pts): The character is descended from a particularly noteworthy member of her house, perhaps a hero of the Symbiot Wars or the Barbarian Invasions. In any case, the character enjoys both the benefits of her ancestry and the responsibility placed on her to live up to her illustrious relative. Player and gamemaster should work together to come up with the identity and deeds of the famous ancestor because others will undoubtedly bring the subject up in the character's presence.

Afflictions

Infamous Ancestor (+1-4 pts): The character is descended from a particularly notorious member of his house, perhaps a coward in battle or a particularly inept diplomat who brought disgrace upon the house. The character will have to overcome the social stigma attached to his relative's bad reputation over and over again. Player and

gamemaster should agree on the identity and deeds of the infamous ancestor, since others will whisper behind the character's back about his tainted past.

Community

Benefices

Royal Patron (1-11 pts): The character has somehow acquired the patronage of a member of one of the five Royal Houses. This may simply be a Hawkwood knight who has taken the character under his wing or it may be a powerful noble who sees in the character the son/daughter he/she never had and who lavishes on the character a great deal of attention. The cost of this Benefice varies according to the actual rank and influence of the patron. A knight with little actual power may cost only 1 point, whereas the patronage of Princess Victoria Hawkwood would cost the full 11 points. (Emperor Alexius's patronage is not available through purchase of this Benefice — see Imperial Favor in the Hawkwood chapter.) A character with a patron within her own house usually has an edge in internal dealings and it is more likely that she will rise in house standing a little more easily than characters without such patronage. It is up to the gamemaster as to how much material assistance this Benefice confers upon the character.

Afflictions

Royal Detractor (+1-11 pts): The character has somehow managed to alienate someone within one of the five Royal Houses. The detractor may be a knight or minor noble who bears a childhood grudge against the character or a powerful noble who disapproves of the character (or her parents) for some personal reason. The point bonus this Affliction confers varies according to the actual rank and influence of the detractor. A Hazat knight with little or no real power may equal a one-point bonus, while hostility from Duke Alvarez of House Hawkwood may be worth the full 11 points. (Emperor Alexius is not included in the personages available as possible detractors — see Imperial Disapproval in the Hawkwood chapter.) A character with a detractor in his own house will have more difficulty gaining fair hearings in house disputes when his detractor is present and his rise within the house will probably be slower or marked with obstacles depending on the influence his detractor wields. It is up to the gamemaster to decide whether or not this Affliction confers material penalties as well.

Possessions

Items

House Artifact (1-10 pts): The character begins the game in possession of a legendary weapon, piece of armor or other item significant to his family. Examples of such items include the sword or armor once carried or worn by a hero of his house. The gamemaster should take into consideration the age, Tech Level, history and reputation of the particular item when assigning a point value to it. Antique but serviceable armor worn by Baron Santius, who freed Byzantium Secundus from the First Republic, may be worth as much as the flux sword used by Lord Halsey Hawkwood to drive a Vuldrok chieftain from the gates of the Hawkwood palace on Gwynneth. Being gifted with a weapon once belonging to either Emperor might cost the full 10 points. Both player and gamemaster should agree on a suitable "history" for the item chosen.

Status

Benefices

Claim of Honor (2-6 pts): Some deed the character has performed has so benefited another house that it owes her a significant favor. The character is able to call in this favor at any time (provided circumstances allow it) and can expect repayment in kind. If she salvaged the reputation of a maligned member of another house, she can expect that house to support her if she becomes, in turn, the victim of slander or treachery. The player and gamemaster should work together to come up with the nature of the deed which won this Benefice for the character as well as its point cost.

Afflictions

Debt of Honor (+2-6 pts): The character owes a significant favor to another Royal House and can expect to have that favor called in at some future time (probably when it is least convenient). Until that happens, the character must deal very carefully with any members of the house to which she owes the favor or else she will suffer some penalty to her reputation or worse. The player and gamemaster should determine the nature of the favor done for the character and the bonus points acquired by taking this Affliction.

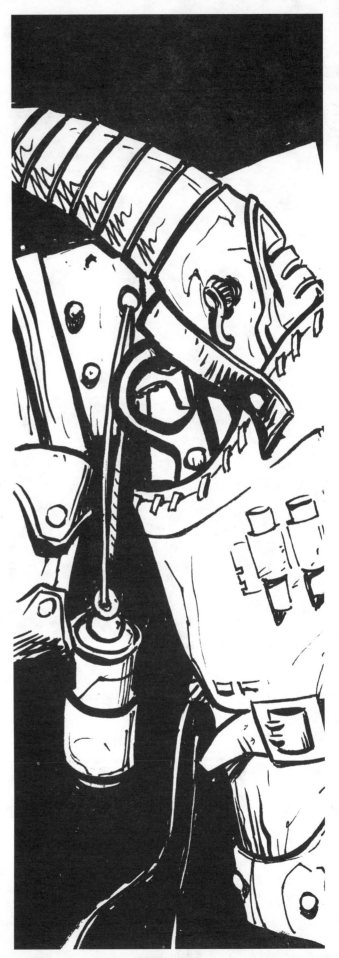

Risen by Pride: House Hawkwood

by Jackie Cassada

"What are the odds, sir?" The young knight peered over the ruined battlements into the starlit darkness beyond. Beside him, Sir Evan Hawkwood raised a pair of IR goggles to his eyes and scanned the horizon.

"Not good," he replied, putting the goggles down and brushing back his sandy curls, now damp with the oppressive evening heat. He turned to his junior officer and placed a hand on his shoulder in a gesture of reassurance. "But not impossible, either. Now go and tell the others to prepare for an imminent attack." Evan smiled slightly as he issued the command. It would never do to let the troops under him see — or hear — his apprehension at their current situation.

Now alone, Evan Hawkwood took a deep breath and tried to compose himself for what might be his final battle. That bastard Konstantin Decados had played him for a fool, hinting that the ancient ruins on the borders of his father's estate on Cadiz might hold the key to ending the state of open hostility between them. He plans to end it, alright, Evan thought grimly. He surveyed the forces arrayed against the handful of Hawkwood knights who had accompanied him to this rendezvous: it was clear that Konstantin had come with a small army of mercenaries. Muster, probably, Evan muttered softly to no one in particular. Ah well, so much for thoughts of a clean death. The Chainers would undoubtedly seek to capture as many as possible, with the intention of making them disappear in one of their slave markets.

"Not a chance," Evan said to the darkness.

"Sir?" His officer was back. "Did you say something?"

Evan shook his head, then returned his attention to the distance, where he thought he detected the faint sound of rapid movement.

"I think they're coming," he said, drawing his flux sword. "Are we ready?"

"Yes, sir," the young knight replied. "We've agreed there'll be no surrender."

Evan nodded grimly. "Of course," he said. "It's the Hawkwood way."

A Proud and Noble Line

Proud traditionalists, stalwart defenders of the rights — and responsibilities — of the nobility as rulers of the Known Worlds, the scions of House Hawkwood bear upon their shoulders the weighty burdens of leadership, respectability and moral rectitude. Though their rise to prominence among the Royal Houses has not been smooth, they have never doubted their fitness to assume their rightful place as champions of order and stability.

Now this proud house stands at the apex of its long history, for one of its own —Alexius Hawkwood — rules the Known Worlds as Emperor. But with this accomplishment has come bitter disappointment, for Emperor Alexius has not been as forthcoming with his largesse as many of his supporters within the house had expected. Instead, House Hawkwood finds itself the victim of Imperial impartiality, forced to stand alongside — rather than above — the other Royal Houses. For most members of the house, this does not present a problem. That the Emperor is a Hawkwood is enough. For others, however, the fruits of victory have turned sour. Beneath the sober facade of a house known for its unshakable honor, discontentment feeds upon resentment and the values which once defined House Hawkwood now face their greatest challenge.

History of the House

Claiming to trace its descent from old Urth's Houses Hapsburg, Windsor and Mountbatten, Hawkwood rose to its position as First House among the Ten through a unique combination of military persistence, diplomatic finesse and personal honor. Coupled with an unshakable belief in its own destiny, these qualities have seen House Hawkwood through periods of ascendancy and decline, propelling it to the heights of temporal power and preserving it in the face of near disaster.

From the Beginning

During the last years of the First Republic, financial mogul Gervaise Windsor-Hapsburg secured control of the planet Delphi, ostensibly to safeguard the mining of rare mineral resources necessary to starship technology. Although official records from that chaotic time name Windsor-Hapsburg as the planet's "administrator," other documents indicate the transfer of outright ownership of Delphi from the First Republic to "a private concern" in return for "material considerations." Upon his arrival, Windsor-Hapsburg discovered himself in possession of a world on the verge of revolution and undertook the herculean task of restoring stability to Delphi. Drawing on his considerable financial resources as well as his own personal military force, Windsor-Hapsburg placed Delphi under martial law and arrested the leaders of the incipient rebellion.

Instead of bringing the rebels to trial, Windsor-Hapsburg took stock of the qualifications presented by the would-be popular leaders of Delphi's dissatisfied populace. Never one to let talent go to waste, Gervaise formed a new coalition government with his erstwhile enemies and declared Delphi an independent planet. From this meeting of old money and new ideals, a noble lineage was born. The house became known by the name of Gervaise's successor, Robert Hawkwood, his daughter's son through

marriage to one of the rebels. Robert's family proudly traced their lineage to Sir John Hawkwood, an English adventurer who rose to fame as a *condottieri* in Italy during Machiavelli's time. The new house, encompassing the lines of Windsor, Hapsburg, Mountbatten and now Hawkwood, embraced a tradition that encompassed a strict code of honor (the product of the ideologies of the former rebels) enhanced by the military expertise of Gervaise' personal troops as well as his own pragmatic approach to problem-solving.

House Hawkwood — and Delphi — prospered under the leadership of Gervaise Windsor-Hapsburg and his grandson. By the time of Robert's death, in 2610, the members of Delphi's new ruling class, now considered "nobility," were beginning to look beyond the confines of their world. Zenobiah Hawkwood, Robert's daughter, assumed the primary position of Planetary Governor and head of House Hawkwood. During her rule, House Hawkwood established control of the independent planet Ravenna through the marriage of her son Trevor to Marianne Mountbatten, the daughter and heir of Ravenna's Supreme Chief.

As the First Republic crumbled, newly independent planets engaged in wars and diplomatic maneuvers as they sought to establish their own power bases. For a time, House Hawkwood attempted to remain aloof from these conflicts, content to consolidate its modest holdings.

Leadership of House Hawkwood continued to pass from generation to generation through the descendants of Gervaise.

Trade with other planets, many of which had come under the control of other self-styled Royal Houses, remained vital to the economic survival of both Delphi and Ravenna. House Hawkwood embarked on a series of carefully orchestrated alliances with a number of other noble families, notable among them the still small but vital House Juandaastas and the Ravenna-based House Trusnikron. When an attempted alliance with one of the chief families of Gwynneth resulted in the vicious murder of Analise Hawkwood, Lord Cyprian Hawkwood launched an invasion fleet to subdue the planet and avenge his daughter's death. After a long and bloody war of attrition, made more difficult due to the intervention of military units from House Decados in support of the locals, Gwynneth fell to the Hawkwood onslaught and became the third world to fly the banner of the lion. During this conflict, Hawkwood knights cemented their reputation as skilled warriors.

During the Ur-Ukar War, House Hawkwood ingratiated itself with the Universal Church through its military actions on behalf of Human Space. Additionally, under the leadership of Princess Augusta Hawkwood, House Hawkwood gave its protection to the Ur-Obun homeworld, bringing that planet under its aegis. With the acquisition of the planet Leminkainen, through a judicious combination of diplomacy and military force, Hawkwood secured control of one of the few sources of the rare mineral Pygmallium, thus leading to alliances with many high-tech consortiums, progenitors of the post-Fall Engineers Guild.

With the rise of the Second Republic, House Hawkwood embarked on a period of intense diplomatic maneuvering designed to secure its place in the new coalition of mercantile interests and Church authority. Prince Geoffrey Hawkwood engineered a series of astute marriages and liaisons among the other houses, including Houses al-Malik, Li Halan, Alecto and Windsor (distantly related to Hawkwood's founder). Alliances with respected Church families also strengthened the Hawkwood position with that increasingly powerful organization.

During the height of the Second Republic's power, House Hawkwood availed itself of the remarkable technological advancements, again relying on the formation of alliances and trade agreements to maintain its advantage. Branching out to some of the crafter families throughout the Known Worlds, House Hawkwood acquired the allegiance of the Ambrim family of Tethys, manufacturers of starships and the finest starship energy shield makers. During the Dark Ages, this arrangement would bring the house into close contact with the Charioteers, who monopolized jumpgate technology and thus controled the passage of traffic between the stars. In a time when the Royal Houses found themselves scrambling to

The Lion and the Mantis: the Hawkwood-Decados Enmity

As a result of the occupation of Gwynneth, evidence linking House Decados to the murder of Analise came to light. The presence of a small Decados delegation, mentioned in a communication from Analise to her father shortly before her death, prompted an investigation conducted by Lord Cyprian himself. A close interrogation of Fergal ap Llwyn, whose marriage to Analise would have brought Gwynneth peacefully into the Hawkwood fold, revealed that he had received a similar offer of marriage to the sister of Duke Zgismund Decados along with veiled threats of dire consequences should he refuse the offer. Angered at the Decados effrontery, Fergal determined to proceed with his marriage to Analise Hawkwood. On the morning of the ceremony, Analise was discovered dead in her chambers, her throat cut. The Decados agents were nowhere to be found.

Instead, Fergal found his lands under assault from rival lords of Gwynneth, assisted in their efforts by off-world military advisors who offered to help overthrow the traitor who would sell the planet to a "foreign interest." Lord Cyprian concluded that these "advisors" were, in fact, the missing Decados delegates and that their intention was to take control of the planet before House Hawkwood could arrive in force. Unfortunately, they miscalculated both the rapidity of Lord Cyprian's response to Analise's death and the implacable persistence of the Hawkwood military machine. None of the so-called advisors turned up among either the rosters of the dead or on the lists of prisoners taken by the victorious Hawkwood armies.

House Hawkwood made a formal complaint to Duke Zgismund in the aftermath of Lord Cyprian's investigation. The duke denied any involvement in Gwynneth's internal matters, instead congratulating Lord Cyprian on his daughter's "courageous act of self-sacrifice to further her father's expansionist ambitions." The outright slur to his honor so enraged Lord Cyprian that he swore a formal vendetta against House Decados, thus beginning the rivalry that has continued to the present.

keep up with the booming mercantile and technological conglomerates that formed the Second Republic's power base, House Hawkwood managed to remain near — if not actually in — the thick of things. Refusing to join the Rogue Worlds in seceding from the Republic, House Hawkwood's leader, Prince Roderick Hawkwood, whose *affair d'amour* with the renowned star pilot Milanza Goforth had already achieved the stature of legend, spoke loudly in denouncing the rebels.

When the Rogue Worlds joined with various alien forces to seize Byzantium Secundus and, with it, the heart of the Second Republic, House Hawkwood saw its moment of glory and claimed it. Prince Roderick's sister, the Duchess General Alexandra Hawkwood, considered the best military mind of the age, is credited in the annals of Hawkwood history with leading the assault that reclaimed Byzantium Secundus from its conquerors. That the pilot of Alexandra's starship was none other than Roderick's lover Milanza Goforth was seen as good fortune at the time. Only later, when some of the other Royal Houses complained that they would have reached Byzantium Secundus ahead of the Hawkwood fleet had they not come up against unexpected delays in passing through the jumpgates, were questions raised as to just how "lucky" Alexandra actually was. Nevertheless, the reclamation of Byzantium Secundus from the rebels took the combined efforts of many Royal Houses, and House Hawkwood was only too happy to share the victory with its allies in Houses Li Halan and al-Malik. They were less pleased with their forced alliance with House Decados, who joined the assault on Byzantium Secundus at the last moment. With the retaking of Byzantium Secundus and the formation of the Ten Houses, the death knell of the Second Republic sounded throughout the Known Worlds. The age of the Royal Houses had arrived.

Beyond the Second Republic

With the demise of the Second Republic in 4000, House Hawkwood was in good position to solidify its leadership of the Ten Houses. Prince Roderick seemed an ideal candidate around which to build a galactic empire. Unfortunately, House Hawkwood's confederates in war did not prove as loyal in peace. Most distressing was the apparent defection of House Windsor from the Hawkwood camp. Count Jasper Windsor's denunciation of General Alexandra Hawkwood's stolen march on Byzantium Secundus did not seriously damage her reputation, but it did open a rift between the two distantly related houses. Houses Li Halan and Alecto, likewise, withdrew some of their favor from House Hawkwood. An impending marriage between Alexandra Hawkwood's son Victor and Leonora Alecto failed to materialize when the Church voiced its disapproval of the match, citing Victor Hawkwood's cybernetic enhancements as grounds of suspected heresy. Although no actual proof could be established, many members of House Hawkwood blamed Decados influence for their sudden reversal in fortunes.

Prince Roderick's unexpected suicide was the final blow to Hawkwood ambitions. An inquiry conducted by the Church concluded that the Hawkwood leader died from self-induced poison aboard his personal starship (piloted, as usual, by Milanza Goforth). Rather than pursue the matter further, possibly implicating Goforth and — by extension — her allies among the piloting guilds, House Hawkwood swallowed the bitter verdict and cut its losses with as much dignity as possible. In a seemingly unrelated incident later, no direct link could be established between the presence on Severus of the Scraver assassin known throughout the Known Worlds as "The Dark Blade" and the disappearance of Gitano Decados, one of the house's most charismatic members, but rumors persisted that Roderick's son and heir, Gordon Hawkwood, was ultimately responsible for the incident.

Its plans for building an empire with themselves in the Imperial seat thwarted temporarily, House Hawkwood staged a strategic retreat from the political arena, concentrating instead on consolidating its planetary holdings, building up its armies, gaining the trust and support of the people under its rule and biding its time. A major restructuring of the house's internal affairs resulted in the abdication of Gordon Hawkwood from his position of leadership in favor of his sister Justine, a methodical administrator who applied herself to the task of quietly increasing Hawkwood influence behind the scenes.

This is not to say that the period known as "The New Dark Ages" to some and "The Age of Nobles" to others held no instances of Hawkwood glory. Setting its sights on ending the rivalry between the Universal Church and the nobility, Hawkwood ambassadors began a campaign to bring the two powers together. Baron Michael Hawkwood became a Church knight, swearing to protect the Orthodox faithful, while Princess Justine's third son Gregory married an Orthodox bishop. Many Hawkwood nobles contributed financially to the Church's mission. Finally, Duke Lawrence Hawkwood, the house's premier diplomat, was instrumental in bringing about the Doctrine of the Privilege of Martyrs, which preserved the use of technology as a noble privilege. Although its place in the Church's hierarchy of supporters would later be supplanted by House Li Halan, in the early years following the fall of the Second Republic, Hawkwood enjoyed a reputation as faithful adherents to the Orthodoxy.

Other Hawkwood nobles found new proving grounds to test their mettle, setting out to put down pockets of rebellion on planets ruled by allied houses. Although they joined in the doomed crusade to break the back of the newly formed Merchant League, House Hawkwood confined its actions to the lesser guilds, leaving the Charioteers and Engineers scrupulously alone.

Starting Over

Little by little, House Hawkwood slowly climbed to prominence again, demonstrating its usefulness to the Ten Houses and the Church in countless ways. When the Merchant League muscled its way into the corridors of power, forcing a triple alliance of nobles, Church and guilds, Hawkwood accepted the presence of the "mercantile element" with as much grace as it could muster. Attracted by the technological superiority of the Merchant League, Hawkwood sought to strengthen its existing contacts within the guilds, most notably among the Charioteers and the Society of Engineers, as well as establishing new connections with the Reeves. In addition to its Church ties, this gave it a foothold in all of the significant power bases. Though Hawkwoods did not compromise their bloodlines through marriage with guild members, other alliances between Hawkwood nobles and the merchant guilds — based on trade —served just as well. Emulating the late Prince Roderick, some younger members of House Hawkwood continued the practice of taking lovers from among the Charioteers, beginning what would eventually be referred to as the "unspoken tradition" of House Hawkwood. By the middle of the fifth millennium, House Hawkwood was once again poised to make its move and nothing short of a full scale invasion from outside the civilized worlds could stop it.

The Barbarian Invasions provided just that impediment. Since the planets controlled by Hawkwood were nearest the jumpgates used by the invaders from beyond the "civilized worlds," Hawkwood initially suffered the worst depredations from the plunderers. The border world of Leminkainen received the worst battering, but the other Hawkwood worlds — including the homeworld of Delphi — suffered heavily from raiders. Although Hawkwood forces were able to drive off the invaders, the damage to their holdings and their finances was catastrophic. With an almost missionary fervor, Hawkwood dropped its political aspirations and concentrated on purging its lands and holdings of the barbarians. For Hawkwood militants, this was their finest hour. The exploits of Generals Malcolm and Vanessa Hawkwood approached legendary status as these cousins and rivals racked up victories along the frontiers of the Known Worlds.

Again, suspicion fell on House Decados for inciting the barbarian invasions of Hawkwood space. Duels of honor between the two houses reached an all-time high. Adrian Hawkwood, heir to the rulership of Gwynneth, and Soldari Decados, younger son of the ruler of Cadiz, personally fought more than fifty duels to first blood. Rumors began to surface that the two young nobles, who sought out every possible opportunity to continue their personal feud, shared a closer bond than hatred. Finally, in a rare instance of Hawkwood-Decados cooperation, both houses intervened to forbid any further dueling between the perpetual rivals. Adrian Hawkwood was shipped to the Obun homeworld and ordered to remain as part of the token Hawkwood presence on that planet; Soldari Decados quietly dropped out of sight.

Prelude to Empire

When Vladimir Alecto, in 4540, announced his intention as leader of the Ten to bring peace and unity to the Known Worlds, stamping out once and for all the barbarian threat, Prince Gervaise Hawkwood II threw his house's support behind Vladimir's enterprise. Despite his

realization of the implications should Alecto's campaign succeed, Prince Gervaise II sent his daughter Zella and his two oldest sons, Winston and Fitzhugh, to serve under Vladimir's command. Excellence recognizes its own, and countless centuries of military expertise forced House Hawkwood to accept that Vladimir offered the best hope for ending the chaos brought about by the barbarian disruption of stable planetary relations. Swallowing their disappointment that the spotlight belonged to another house, they joined wholeheartedly in the crusade. That it offered more opportunities for personal glory to younger members of the house was an extra inducement.

The annals of Hawkwood history contain numerous accounts of the courage and daring of countless heroes from this period. Both Zella and Winston Hawkwood covered themselves in glory with their bold forays into barbarian space and the reclamation of their worlds from the clutches of the invaders. Fitzhugh's career might have equaled that of his siblings had it not ended tragically in a suicidal charge against a numerically superior barbarian fleet in order to delay them long enough for Alecto's personal army to overcome them.

The civil war that erupted after Vladimir's victory over the barbarians posed a moral quandary for many within House Hawkwood. Alecto's refusal to return to their owners some of the worlds he had reclaimed drove a number of Royal Houses to rebellion against the man whom they considered to have betrayed them. The presence of House Decados among the rebels finally clinched Hawkwood's stand, however, and they joined with Alecto's supporters to assist in the formation of the Empire, with Vladimir as the first — though shockingly short-lived — Emperor.

Although the assassination of Emperor Vladimir during his coronation ceremony horrified House Hawkwood, it nevertheless threw open opportunity's door. During the turbulent struggles which followed, House Hawkwood managed to maintain its strength while other Royal Houses — including House Alecto — fell by the wayside. As usual, Hawkwood accused Decados of complicity in Vladimir's assassination; this time, however, Decados rallied with an accusation of its own, pointing out that General Zella Hawkwood had received a private audience with Vladimir just prior to his coronation. Open war almost broke out between the two houses, but the intercession of House Li Halan as well as direct threats by the patriarch to excommunicate both house heads prevented a potentially disastrous conflict.

Due to the ravages of Vladimir's campaign against the barbarians, many Royal Houses had become extinct, among them House Windsor, thus leaving House Hawkwood as the primary inheritor (through its founder Gervaise Windsor-Hapsburg) of many Windsor properties (none of them planets)... and all of their debts. The number of Royal Houses in contention for the vacant Imperial throne was reduced to five. Unfortunately, however,

those competitors rivaled Hawkwood in strength and influence.

Although the prospect of exercising occasional power through the office of regent seemed pale in comparison with the Imperial title, Hawkwood again faced the inevitable with its seemingly boundless store of dignity and stoicism. When Lady Avyryl Hawkwood married Halvor Li Halan, then Bishop of Kish, and helped lobby for his appointment to the 10-year position of Universal Regent, she had no foreknowledge of her husband's growing ambitions to unite secular and religious power bases into a theocratic government. Even when House Hawkwood attempted to stir up rebellion among the Royal Houses against Halvor's dual title of Regent and Patriarch, Lady Avyryl remained loyal to her husband despite placing herself at odds with her house. Her supporters claim she renounced her Hawkwood allegiance out of love; her detractors insisted that her own ambitions caused her to cast her lot with the power of the Church and the Li Halan.

In the wake of Halvor's death, House Hawkwood realized it must move quickly to prevent his son Constantine from succeeding him. Backed by House Hazat, House Hawkwood brought about the end of the short-lived theocratic experiment, thus gaining massive status among the other Royal Houses, who also opposed such an extreme shift in the balance of power.

The Final Hurdle

The Symbiot Wars, which began in 4900, put a damper on other considerations as all the resources of the Known Worlds were marshaled against a nearly unbeatable foe. Once again, House Hawkwood distinguished itself in battle after battle. A new generation of Hawkwood heroes arose, notable among them Grania Hawkwood, whose psychic abilities — considered an aberration within the house — made her an ideal combatant in the war against the parasitic enemy. The exploits of the Penitent General, as she came to be called, combined with those of her close companion (and, some contend, lover), the Eskatonic priestess Mariah Juandaastas, elevated the house's reputation for bravery and daring to a new standard.

By the time the threat was declared officially "over" (at least for the present), Hawkwood had worked its way to the top of the political heap, thanks to the bold maneuvers of Duke Darius Erik Hawkwood. His regency was marked by another intensive spate of political marriages and trade alliances, all with the purpose of strengthening Hawkwood's position in the struggle for the Imperial throne. His plans to acquire greater power among the council of Electors would not bear fruit for several generations, and would, in fact, spark the series of diplomatic and military skirmishes that would come to be known as the Emperor Wars.

The arrival on the political scene of Alexius Hawkwood finally realized the long-standing dream of House Hawkwood. Following in the footsteps of his uncle

Darius, Alexius utilized his own diplomatic acumen and tactical skill to acquire the necessary backing to claim the position of Emperor. After solidly defeating House Li Halan's push for the throne, Alexius received not only the support of the subdued house but the blessings of the Church as well. This, along with the backing of House al-Malik, almost guaranteed his ascendancy to the Imperial throne.

The ensuing battles — led by Houses Decados and Hazat — to contest that claim occupied the newly proclaimed Emperor for a handful of years, but Alexius' forethought and the support of most of the other factions in the Known Worlds prevailed. Through his military prowess as well as the clandestine maneuverings of his close friend, Sir Chamon Mazarin, Alexius managed to defeat both the most militant and the sneakiest of the Royal Houses. Finally, in 4995, Decados and Hazat admitted defeat, accepting Alexius Hawkwood as Emperor and bringing a fragile peace to the stars. House Hawkwood had finally achieved the dream that had powered it for millennia — as it had always known it would.

The Price of Victory

With Emperor Alexius on the throne, House Hawkwood looked forward to its just reward, expecting to fill the most prominent positions in the Empire and to share the governance of the Known Worlds along with its greatest son. Alexius' decision to disassociate himself from his house in order to avoid a show of favoritism came as a rude awakening to the Hawkwoods. Some members of the house feel that they have been abandoned by their Emperor and now taste the bitterness of finding themselves sidelined as Alexius's courts the expertise of the Church, the League and the other Royal Houses. Others point to the fact that the Emperor has salted his council of advisors with its fair share of Hawkwoods, citing his appointment of Sir Chamon Mazarin as chief of Imperial Security as proof that the Emperor has not forgotten the house of his birth.

Hawkwood's current head, Princess Victoria, maintains an aloof silence regarding the Emperor's self-appointed separation. Her quiet administration of house affairs seems to proclaim that whatever the circumstances, House Hawkwood will conduct itself with its customary sense of propriety. Many younger Hawkwood's, particularly those with no great estates to hold them to one spot, have actively sought service in the Emperor's fleets or as Questing Knights and ambassadorial staff. They welcome Alexius's indifference to their position as "kin," feeling that their own merits will attain for them the rank and recognition they deserve.

One of Alexius's most outspoken critics, however, is also his closest relative. His brother, Alvarex Hawkwood, has lent his protection and assistance to a faction of malcontents within the house, all of whom expected Imperial favors and were sorely disappointed when they were not forthcoming. The pride and honor which has for so long stood as a hallmark of the house now turns in upon itself, and petty bickering among Hawkwoods becomes more and more common. For perhaps the first time in its long and noble history, House Hawkwood must struggle with internal dissension and face the prospect that, like the darkening suns, its glory may finally begin to fade.

The Making of a Hawkwood Noble

Appearance

Look noble and the world will react accordingly.
— Lady Portia Hawkwood

From childhood, members of House Hawkwood learn the importance of projecting the proper image — one which inspires confidence in subordinates, admiration among peers and respect from foes. This attention to "style" comes not from devotion to superficialities, but from an understanding of the interplay between mind and body. Eschewing transient fashions for "classic" attire, both men and women of the house cultivate stylish conservatism in their dress. Even young members of House Hawkwood are expected to conform to the "house look," and excess in any aspect of clothing or hairstyle receives strong disapprobation from the older generation. Many Hawkwoods affect a military or quasimilitary cut to their clothing. Not for them are the daring couture of Decados or the exotic flair of al Malik. The portraits of past Hawkwoods that hang in the gallery of the family's palace on Delphi are sometimes referred to in jest as the "Gallery of Style," but the joke contains more than a grain of truth. With only minor changes, the Hawkwood styles of the last several centuries can easily stand alongside current house fashion. Combat dress tends toward chain or plate mail, usually of the highest available quality.

Although there is considerable physical variation among Hawkwoods due to intermarriages with most of the other Royal Houses, most members of the house tend to have regular features and dark brown, red or sandy-colored hair. Strong jaws, aquiline noses and wide brows are common facial characteristics, with brown or green eyes predominating. Hawkwoods place great emphasis on physique and fitness, encouraging its members to train their bodies for peak performance — whether in combat or on the ballroom floor. Nevertheless, the more sedentary members of the house often acquire a certain "portliness," particularly as they age.

Codes of Behavior

Act as you would have others act.
— Lady Portia Hawkwood

Although all Royal Houses adhere to certain accepted codes of conduct concerning protocol, hospitality, duel-

ing and courtly affairs (including those of the heart), House Hawkwood defines itself by these customs. From infancy, all Hawkwoods are inundated with the finer points of etiquette and manners, learning how to behave with composure and dignity in any imaginable situation. Titles, forms of address, rules of precedence and other minutiae of diplomatic intercourse are considered part of a basic Hawkwood education. By the time of their first presentation to "society" (around 16 years of age), most Hawkwoods have a working knowledge of heraldry and can recite their lineage for at least ten generations. Cultivation of arts and letters is encouraged as a mark of a well-rounded individual, though too serious an interest in any performing art is looked down upon as effete or eccentric.

House Hawkwood is renowned for its gracious hospitality. Though they are not as lavish as some other Royal Houses, Hawkwood hosts ensure the comfort and protection of their guests — even members of House Decados. Polite to a fault, particularly to those they despise or consider inferior, House Hawkwood uses hospitality as a double-edged sword, garnering favors as well as ensuring that no censure can be laid at their door for mistreatment of visitors.

Despite its disapproval by the Church, duels of honor are meat and drink to many younger Hawkwoods and not a few older members of the house still bear scars from youthful (or not so youthful) encounters on the dueling field. Sticklers for protocol, Hawkwood duelists adhere to strict rules. Any Hawkwood caught cheating or using underhanded tactics in a duel receives the full brunt of her family's disapproval, regardless of the outcome. Many expert duelists in the house actually keep "books" on various members of other houses, noting their combat idiosyncracies, strengths and weakness for the express purpose of taking advantage of these factors on the field of honor.

Courtship and marriage within House Hawkwood likewise follows proscribed paths, and most marital unions are arranged early in a young Hawkwood's life. Alliances with friendly houses are common, but occasionally marriages become ways of settling grievances or easing tensions between potential rivals. The glaring exception lies in the singular absence of Decados-Hawkwood marriages. While marriages between House Hawkwood and the League are rare, there are a handful of such unions involving Charioteer partners, who are then "adopted" into the house and given a title of some sort to legitimize their presence.

Amorous liaisons outside of marriage are winked at provided both parties conduct their affairs with discretion and do nothing to disgrace the Hawkwood reputation. In fact, the stability of most Hawkwood marriages has often been attributed to the tolerance of both husband and wife for the romantic involvements of the other. That more notoriety does not attach itself to House Hawkwood is a testimony to its circumspection.

Rising in Rank

Ascend by merit, fall by misadventure.
— Lady Portia Hawkwood

Although the lines of inheritance of Hawkwood lands and property generally follow the custom of primogeniture, in which the oldest child receives the bulk (if not all) of the estate, House Hawkwood also tries to ensure that future generations earn what they inherit. All Hawkwoods spend their early adulthood in some form of military or ambassadorial service to the house. Here they practice the traits that have been drilled into them from youth: courage, self-discipline, patience, diplomacy and, above all, honor.

Before exercising any real administrative power within the house, young Hawkwoods embark on a "tour of duty" that takes them to all the Hawkwood controlled worlds, where they acquire an on-site education concerning the house's holdings, resources and subjects. Thus, even though a Hawkwood noble may be heir to the Barony of Kelster on Gwynneth, she also has a thorough grasp of the importance of the Pygmallium mines on Leminkainen, the problems involved in training urrocs on Ravenna, the political importance of Delphi and the diplomatic delicacy necessary when dealing with the natives of Obun.

With the exception of knighthoods, titles within House Hawkwood are hereditary —contingent on the proper maintenance of the lands that accrue to the title. Permanent loss of lands usually implies the loss of the title that goes with it: if a Hawkwood baron loses his barony to barbarians or a warring house, he must either reclaim it within ten years or else distinguish himself in some material fashion lest he face the possible loss of his title. Even knighthoods must be earned, however, and in House Hawkwood, deeds speak for themselves.

Knighthood is conferred upon deserving Hawkwoods by ranking family members and forms the indisputable "right of passage" into full house membership. To gain acknowledgment as a knight, a Hawkwood must demonstrate her bravery in battle —usually through some action against outworld barbarians or rebel groups on Hawkwood-controlled worlds — or else must participate in some successful diplomatic mission (acknowledged as a different kind of "war").

The history of House Hawkwood is replete with examples of legendary feats of courage, particularly in the early years of the Symbiot War, when Hawkwood generals led hopeless missions against the parasitic enemy in the defense of Stigmata. The Barbarian Invasions also demonstrated Hawkwood leadership and military acumen in the preservation and recovery of their besieged planets. Even more common are the less exciting but no less important tales of shrewd diplomatic maneuvers that increased the influence of the house. Every Hawkwood worthy of the name aspires to have her own deeds recorded in the annals of the house.

Service with the Imperial Fleet provides one avenue for achieving honor and glory, and many young Hawkwood knights take advantage of this opportunity to defend the Empire. Others, desirous of attaining truly legendary status, seek their fortunes on the frontiers of Known Space, hoping to discover Lost Worlds to add to their house's holdings. The elite Questing Knights promote the expansionist aims of the house — and also channel the more reckless and adventuresome Hawkwoods away from areas where they might cause trouble.

Allies and Enemies

Marry those whom you cannot best on the battlefield.
— Lady Portia Hawkwood

House Hawkwood, perhaps more than many other houses, realizes that it cannot exist in a social vacuum and has spent most of its existence forging alliances among those groups — noble and otherwise — who can help them preserve their prominence and influence in the Empire. In addition, the strong ambitions of House Hawkwood have won it a few powerful enemies, who would like nothing better than to see them fade into anonymity or, even better, extinction.

Noble Houses

House Decados: The longstanding rivalry between House Hawkwood and House Decados has often assumed epic proportions. Hawkwood blames House Decados for most of its setbacks, even those in which that house could not possibly have played a role. The fact that it can never seem to prove its suspicions adds fuel to the flame of its hatred. House Hawkwood considers Decados as only marginally noble and ascribes to it a litany of vile attributes. Meetings between members of these two houses on the diplomatic battleground are almost as bloody and vicious as their encounters on the dueling field. Watching one house claim the hospitality of the other provides spectators with boundless amusement as the two rivals attempt to outdo each other in venomous courtesy and malicious politeness.

House al Malik: Their close alliance with Alexius Hawkwood in his bid for the Imperial throne has solidified the bonds between Houses Hawkwood and al-Malik. Marriages between the two houses are common, and friendships formed in youth between members of al-Malik and Hawkwood often last a lifetime. The combination of al-Malik's vibrant passion and Hawkwood's sober practicality results in a perfectly complementary balance between these great Royal Houses, despite their sometimes different aims.

House Juandaastas: Its shared interest in the Ur-Obun as well as its presence on Gwynneth and other Hawkwood worlds has gained this minor house the respect of House Hawkwood. House Hawkwood's efforts to ensure protec-

tion for intelligent nonhuman species have ensured that House Juandaastas will remain solidly in the Hawkwood camp. A few intermarriages between the houses have led some to speculate that Hawkwood is seeking to increase the incidence of psychic ability within its bloodline.

House Trusnikron: This minor house has linked its fortune inextricably with House Hawkwood, serving as trainers of the avian urrocs on Ravenna and forming the core of House Hawkwood's flying cavalry. In return for their diligence, House Hawkwood has granted them holdings on all of their homeworlds (with the exception of Obun) and includes members of House Trusnikron in their retinue. Marriages between the two houses are also common.

The Church

Urth Orthodox: Not surprisingly, the most traditional of houses has actively courted the most traditional faction within the Universal Church. Hawkwood financial support of the Church has done much to quell any doubts once raised about their state of grace, while the cathedrals on Hawkwood homeworlds are visible evidence of the house's desire to remain in the Church's favor.

Brother Battle: House Hawkwood has an active military tradition, and its service in wartime has brought it into close contact with these combat experts. Certain Hawkwoods have sent their second sons or daughters to this order, but these scions grow up with their loyalties firmly wedded to their new order rather than the house of their birth. Members of Brother Battle can always expect to find hospitality at any Hawkwood holding and their requests for military cooperation are often accepted.

The Merchant League

Charioteers: House Hawkwood realizes the vital role the Charioteers play in space travel and trade. Over the years since the rise of the Merchant League, House Hawkwood has made certain that its relationship with this essential guild remains one of mutual respect and cooperation. Charioteers are frequently found among the retinue of younger Hawkwoods. During the Barbarian Invasions, the house depended heavily on this guild's mastery of the jumproutes to enable it to successfully repel the raiders' incursions.

Engineers: Like most Royal Houses, Hawkwood enjoys the benefits technology affords. As the caretakers of that technology, the Engineers command the respect and, some say, the clandestine financial support of House Hawkwood. At any rate, members of House Hawkwood usually have little difficulty obtaining necessary technology when they have need of it. The house can certainly afford to avail itself of some of the Engineers' most sophisticated and least obtrusive cyber-enhancements, particularly in the realm of prosthetics. Some veterans of the Barbarian Invasions are rumored to owe "an arm and a leg" to the Engineers.

Others

Ur-Obun: Hawkwood protection of the Obun homeworld has garnered much prestige for the house from those who appreciate the diplomatic expertise and spiritual wisdom of these peaceful and cultured aliens. Although they do not go as far as House Juandaastas in their close relations with the Obun, House Hawkwood often avails itself of the services of Obun psychics and ambassadors.

Vuldrok: Aside from House Decados, no other group of people arouses the anger and indignation of House Hawkwood like these barbarians whose territory borders Hawkwood space. A Hawkwood will often leave the vicinity if a Vuldrok representative is present — one of the few breaches of diplomatic protocol committed by members of the house with any regularity. That they nevertheless permit Vuldrok ambassadors passage through their space en route to Byzantium Secundus proves their pragmatism rather than their tolerance for the despoilers of civilized space.

Holdings

House Hawkwood controls the worlds of Delphi, Gwynneth, Leminkainen and Ravenna. In addition, it exercises official governance of the Obun homeworld although that planet is technically an independent world. The following descriptions of Hawkwood holdings illustrates the variety of resources available to the house. The fact that Vuldrok space abuts Hawkwood's territory has forced that house to divert much of its attention and resources to securing their borders. Many Hawkwood worlds are in the process of recovering from bearing the brunt of barbarian raids.

Delphi

Massive terraforming has made Delphi similar to old Urth in its terrain, with a wide variety of climates ranging from arctic to tropical and a diverse biota. In a few places, notably on the island continent of Courai, indigenous flora and fauna have been preserved.

Princess Victoria Hawkwood exercises sovereignty over the planet, which boasts a population of over two billion humans and nearly a hundred thousand aliens. Some rare minerals are found on Delphi and a long-standing agreement with House Justinian allows that minor house to oversee the mining interests on the planet.

The homeworld of House Hawkwood enjoys a relatively high level of technology, with several large cities boasting Second Republic technology. Most of the world, particularly in the less settled regions, exists in less sophisticated conditions: electricity is available to freemen classes, but the serfs who are responsible for most of the planet's food production live medieval lives. This planet is the center of Hawkwood activity and most nobles, even if they have holdings elsewhere, maintain individual residences in the capital.

Gwynneth

Much of this world is still covered by old growth forests, simulating the ancient woods that once reportedly blanketed Holy Terra. Although its population numbers nearly a billion, this does not include the uncounted groups of pagan peoples residing in the deep backwoods of the planet. The lumber industry provides Gwynneth with its major export, both in raw material and in finely crafted furnishings.

The Hawkwood nobles who maintain estates on Gwynneth also keep a constant watch for signs of Vuldrok interference with the planet. Gwynneth suffered major losses of life and property from the Vuldrok Raiders. Unfortunately, the pagan population of the planet saw the Raiders as liberators come to free them from the yoke of a Church-dominated Empire. House Hawkwood, in order to bolster its military presence on the planet, has hired Muster mercenaries from Bannockburn, thus giving the Chainers a less than welcome inroad on the world and resulting in some friction between the locals and the auxiliaries.

Even in the larger population centers such as the capital city of Llanfyrth, technology rarely exceeds Victorian-age capabilities. The exceptions are, of course, found in those places where the Hawkwoods actually maintain estates and residences, where Second Republic technology maintains house members in comfort. The "forest people," a Hawkwood euphemism for the pagans, dwell in hovels that barely approach medieval standards of sophistication.

Leminkainen

Closer than any of the Known Planets to the Vuldrok Border, Leminkainen presents House Hawkwood with a bureaucratic and military nightmare. Overrun at one point during the Barbarian Invasions, Leminkainen is still playing catch-up, trying to recover from the damage done to its cities and farmlands. Although House Hawkwood was able to retake their planet and drive out most of the invaders, many barbarians remained behind after their armies left and now form their own enclave on one of the three major landmasses of the planet. While claiming sovereignty over what they call Valdalla, these tribes maintain a tenuous truce with the Hawkwood "overlords," whom they refuse to acknowledge as such though they pay tribute to them anyway.

Leminkainen is valuable to House Hawkwood because of the presence of rare deposits of Pygmallium. An entire Hawkwood garrison resides on the site where this precious metal is extracted in order to protect the area from possible attack. The population of Leminkainen is less than 500,000 (not counting the barbarians, who have never submitted to a census). Most of the inhabitants of the planet live in small villages where they spend their time laboring long hours to make the land produce once more and to help it recover from the hardships and depredations caused by long years of pitched battles. The city

of Hakkonen, the largest on the planet, lies near both Leminkainen's only starport and the Pygmallium mines.

The Engineers have an agreement with House Hawkwood that allows them access to the Pygmallium produced on planet in return for reduced rates for acquiring and repairing advanced technology. They also maintain a minor guildhouse on the planet.

Ravenna

This planet contains some of the most striking geographic features to be found on any of the Hawkwood controlled worlds: towering mountains and arid deserts vie with lush woodlands and sprawling plains. Although it supports a human population of less than half a billion, its mineral resources provide House Hawkwood with vital income. Many of the inhabitants work the mines of Ravenna and the planet houses several fine smiths and artisans who shape the metals extracted from the earth into tools, weapons and decorative objects. Swords of Ravennan steel are among the favored weaponry of Hawkwood knights.

As the birthplace of Emperor Alexius, who comes from Sardonia, its capital city, Ravenna has recently become inundated with visitors eager to see for themselves the place that gave birth to the Savior of the Empire. Hawkwood nobility often gathers on the grand estates that surround the environs of the capital to enjoy such pastimes as hunting, falconry contests and to test their prowess at riding the magnificent urrocs trained on the planet by members of House Trusnikron.

In many ways, Ravenna is a showcase planet: technology levels for the peasantry are kept deliberately low to preserve the idyllic atmosphere of the villages that dot the countryside near the Hawkwood estates and preserves. The annual Craftsman's Fair held in the Agora in Sardonia draws visitors from throughout the Known Worlds to admire the local talent and purchase for themselves some unique example of "peasant craft."

If the peasantry is unhappy with its enforced backwardness, it gives no sign of it, seeming content to toil under the gentle rule of its Hawkwood rulers.

Obun

The natural beauty of this planet is accentuated by Obun architectural philosophy, which strives to complement rather than overpower its surroundings. As planetary rulers, House Hawkwood maintains a governmental enclave and a small military presence here but otherwise leaves Obun to its indigenous population. A few members of House Juandaastas also reside here with their Obun spouses.

The bulk of the Obun live here, and their laws take precedence over those of the Empire in purely internal matters. The technology level is relatively sophisticated; though it differs in design, it falls somewhere between Diaspora and Early Second Republic in complexity. Nevertheless, students of architecture make pilgrimages to

Obun to marvel at the alien sense of design and come back with a new sense of how to blend nature and technology into a harmonious whole.

Personages

As a house noted for its emphasis on personal pride and honor, House Hawkwood has its share of distinguished individuals. Many point to Emperor Alexius Hawkwood as the epitome of Hawkwood achievement and distinction, while others maintain that he is only one in a long list of notables — the greatest so far, perhaps, but still far from unique in the history of the house. The following selection of individuals illustrates the variety of personalities that have brought fame and, sometimes, infamy to this noblest of Royal Houses.

Princess Victoria Hawkwood

From her palatial estate on Delphi, Princess Victoria sets the standards for House Hawkwood — and they are high ones. Now in her early forties, Victoria Hawkwood presents a formidable appearance even toward those closest to her. Tall and slim, with a grace born from years of schooling in fencing and dance, she carries herself with the natural poise of a born leader. Never considered a ravishing beauty, she is thought of as a "strikingly handsome woman" by her admirers and a "hard-faced harridan" by her foes. She is, or can be, both.

An intensely private person, Princess Victoria keeps her own counsel and has never been known to lose her temper in public. Her self-control, at times, frightens those who realize the constant pressure she is under from underlings who beset her with demands to exert her influence on the Emperor to publicly acknowledge his family ties. Princess Victoria meets all such suggestions with a coolness that quickly ends the discussion. Her position seems to be that, regardless of who sits on the Imperial throne, House Hawkwood must continue to deal, day in and day out, with the other factions in the Empire. Alexius will not be Emperor forever, and House Hawkwood must remain strong and self-reliant in order to survive. With her at its helm, few doubt that they will succeed in their effort.

Duke Alvarex Hawkwood

Alexius's younger brother (by a year), Duke Alvarex Hawkwood bears a strong enough physical resemblance to the Emperor that he is occasionally mistaken for him by those who have never seen the two of them together. Once a staunch supporter of his brother's rise to power, now the duke finds himself increasingly critical of Alexius's policies, particularly those which emphasize the Emperor's determination to downplay his house affiliations. Lacking Alexius's charismatic manner, Alvarex more often alienates those whose favor he attempts to court. Despite this, his military expertise makes him a valuable tactician whose services are often sought by the Imperial Fleet — a force which Alvarex believes he should com-

mand in his brother's name.

Duke Alvarex maintains an extensive estate on Ravenna; in fact, it was his brother's estate until Alexius assumed the throne and ceded it to his brother. Here the duke hosts many like-minded family members, treating them to hunting parties and gala festivities, hoping to win their support for instituting a Hawkwood lobby on Byzantium Secundus (among them, Count Faustus Hawkwood). Unfortunately, his off-putting personality works against him and it seems unlikely that his efforts to insinuate himself into his brother's counsel will succeed without divine intervention. To this effect, some say, Alvarex has begun courting influential members of the Orthodoxy.

Baroness Morgein Hawkwood

Roguishly handsome and devastatingly charismatic, Morgein Hawkwood is at one and the same time one of the most popular and most scandalous members of her house. At 29 years, she displays the distinctive Hawkwood physique — but parts company with the standard "look" in all other ways. She is partial to the exotic dress of the al-Malik, although she sometimes sports the gritty, no-nonsense attire popular among the Muster. Rumors abound that the Rogue Baroness, as she is called in social circles, is actually the issue of her mother, Lady Augusta Hawkwood (now deceased) and a Decados lover. Although Morgein has undoubtedly heard these rumors, she has never addressed them directly to confirm or deny them — adding a spark of veracity to the speculations.

Her small estate on Ravenna is administered in her absence by her aunt, Lady Elwynn, since the Baroness prefers to spend her time aboard her private ship jaunting from planet to planet, inflicting herself on the hospitality of whatever house rules there. She is one of the few Hawkwoods to actively seek the company of younger members of Houses Decados and Hazat, thumbing her nose at family members who accuse her of treachery.

Notorious for her general disregard of the usual protocols of "courtly love," Morgein flaunts her multiple lovers, sometimes arriving at an official function unannounced and with a trio (or more) of paramours in her train. The baroness also has contacts among the Scravers and the Engineers, and many suspect that she has availed herself of more than one cybernetic implant. Her far-flung travels have led to gossip that Morgein actually works for the Imperial Eye, using her reprobate lifestyle as a cover for her real activities on behalf of the Empire.

Lord Randall Hawkwood

The younger brother of Baron Clement Hawkwood, who oversees a sizable barony on Gwynneth, Randall has developed a reputation as a populist and a supporter of Gwynneth's "forest people" — the pagan tribes that dwell deep within the planet's vast forests. Disapproved of by his brother and nearly thrown out of the family for his early support for the rights of serfs and his participation in several failed "peasant actions" against his brother, Randall was exiled for a year and a day by Clement. Forbidden to enter his brother's lands, Randall sought refuge in the wilderness, where he was discovered by a tribe of "tree-worshipping pagans." When he finally resurfaced, after an absence of three years (during which his brother assumed him dead), he emerged as a confirmed advocate of the right of the pagans to live their own lives without persecution from the Church for their heretical beliefs. Some suspect that Randall has, in fact, fallen away from the Church, although he still professes to follow the Orthodox faith. He is considered something of a social embarrassment due to his propensity for publicly defending the pagans at banquets, balls and other occasions for the nobility to gather. Some predict that it is only a matter of time before he comes under the scrutiny of the Inquisition.

Tall and muscular, with dark brown hair and rugged features, Randall Hawkwood disdains the formal attire of his house, preferring to dress in the sturdy, wilderness-friendly garments of the people for whom he acts as spokesman. When he does affect house garb, usually for a rare appearance at some house function, he seems everything a Hawkwood should be — until he holds forth in his crusade for "his" pagans.

Countess Portia Hawkwood

The daughter of an arranged marriage between Sibylla Torenson and the late Phillip Hawkwood, who occupied the governorship of Ravenna before his untimely death while riding his favorite urroc high above the skies of the capitol, Portia Hawkwood has inherited the Torenson grasp of etiquette and protocol. Now approaching sixty, Countess Hawkwood has taken it upon herself to write the definitive guide to Hawkwood comportment and style.

Once considered one of the ten most beautiful women in the galaxy, Portia Hawkwood has glided through three marriages (all arranged) and innumerable love affairs, overseen the weddings of her seven children, managed a sizable estate near one of Ravenna's largest hunting preserves, and dispensed her incomparable knowledge of traditions and proper behavior to several generations of Hawkwoods who have come under her influence. A companion in girlhood to Lady Regnus-Octavia Hawkwood, the Emperor's mother, Countess Hawkwood had a hand in the early education of Alexius and many of her admirers attribute the Emperor's diplomatic skills to her tutelage. Portia, of course, tactfully denies any such claim.

Although her beauty has faded to a whisper of its former glory, Portia still represents the height of fashion and grooming — at least among the elder Hawkwoods. Her lustrous red hair is now an equally luxurious silver crown, while her clear green eyes have not lost a whit of their sharpness. Only a slight hesitation to her step and an occasional tendency to exhaust herself after minor exertions hint of time's encroachment. Many house families send their daughters and sons to stay with her for brief periods during their formative years so that they can absorb some of her good breeding and sense of style and deportment.

Roleplaying
Hawkwood Characters

Every Hawkwood has a purpose. Whether born to rule the Known Worlds (as in the case of Emperor Alexius), to drive the Vuldrok out of civilized space or to hold the record for duels of honor won (and survived), Hawkwoods seem to center themselves around a sense of personal destiny. Even the actions of the most wayward members of the house reflect a highly individualized interpretation of Hawkwood pride and honor.

Besides their penchant for personal honor and unflinching loyalty to their house, Hawkwoods demonstrate a broad range of both positive and negative personality traits. Some house members may possess great courage, personal charisma or an unflappable composure, while others may demonstrate extreme recklessness, disdainful arrogance or sublime indifference. Personality strengths and weaknesses often complement one another: a confident Hawkwood may harbor an inner tendency to doubt herself; an inflexible traditionalist may possess an unconscious rebellious streak. Most Hawkwood nobles believe they were born to lead, and often shoulder the burden of decision-making even when they are not in command of a group. In some cases, this assumption may lead to an internal power struggle, with the odds in favor of the Hawkwood. Some Hawkwoods possess the subtlety to direct a group's actions from the sidelines, using more diplomatic means to influence the nominal leader in the "right" direction.

Hawkwood Stereotypes: Charismatic monarch (King Arthur), diplomatic impresario (Henry Kissinger), military genius (Erwin Rommel), iron-willed leader (Margaret Thatcher), veteran campaigner, charmed daredevil, compulsive competitor, inflexible tyrant, visionary rebel leader.

Gamemastering Hawkwoods

The following ideas may help gamemasters build stories around Hawkwood characters or involve a group in some Hawkwood related struggle.

Lost Honor Restored: Through no fault of her own, a Hawkwood knight (perhaps a player character or a friend of the group) has suffered a severe blow to her reputation and now bears the stigma of coward or (worse) traitor to her house. The characters can help the unfortunate character restore or recover her honor.

Trouble in High Places: A Hawkwood baron's estate shows signs of blatant mismanagement, but the house is attempting to keep this knowledge from leaking to potential rivals. The characters' discreet intervention is necessary to protect House Hawkwood from embarrassment or loss of valuable lands.

Personal Vendetta: A member of House Decados takes a personal interest in ruining the fortunes of a Hawkwood character, who subsequently vows to take revenge on her rival. The characters become caught up in a web of intrigue and treachery. Duels of honor abound.

In the Face of the Enemy: A prominent Vuldrok ambassador needs escorting through Hawkwood space *en route* to an important meeting on Byzantium Secundus. Assigned to see the alien rival safely to his destination, the party realizes that certain members of House Hawkwood would prefer to see their charge quietly "disappear."

Up for Grabs: A Hawkwood noble dies without heir and her lands become available to a worthy inheritor. The house leaders devise a challenging "test of competence" — and the players are in the running.

Traits

Blessings and Curses

The following list of new Blessings and Curses are particularly appropriate for members of House Hawkwood, though some of them may apply to characters from other houses or groups as well.

Appearance

Blessings

Intimidating (1 pt: +1 Impress when convincing others to follow your lead)

Striking (1 pt: +1 Impress in full regalia)

Curses

Milksop (+1 pt: -1 Impress when convincing others to follow your lead)

Nondescript (+1 pt: -1 Charm among strangers)

Behavior

Blessings

Persistent (2 pts: +2 Calm when faced with obstacles to an overriding goal)

Curses

Foolhardy (+2 pts: -2 Wits when confronted with high-risk/high-reward situations)

Knacks

Blessings

Expert Rider (2 pts: +2 Ride with familiar mounts)

Reputation

Blessings

Unimpeachable (2 pts: +2 Extrovert when attempting to inspire trust)

Curses

Rebel (+2 pts: -2 Extrovert among nobility)

Benefices and Afflictions

Status

Benefice

Imperial Favor (1-10 pts): The character has performed some action which has resulted in achieving favorable notice by Emperor Alexius or someone in his court. The more significant the action, the more expensive it is for the character to buy this Benefice. The player and gamemaster should decide at the time of character creation what circumstances resulted in this Benefice and which Imperial courtier favors the character. Possession of this Benefice does not mean that the character can get away with murder; it does, however, indicate that any petitions for Imperial assistance or intervention may receive a warmer hearing than if she did not have Imperial Favor. Others may also react more positively to the character if they know (or think) that doing so will increase their own Imperial standing (note that this is not necessarily true, but many people will assume it is and act accordingly).

1 = You know someone in the lowest rank of Alexius's court

2 = You know a member of the Imperial Guard

4 = You know a distinguished member of the Imperial court (i.e. Sir Chamon Mazarin)

6 = You know one of the Emperor's highest ranking officials (i.e. Bran Botan vo Karm)

8 = You know a member of the Emperor's immediate family

10 = You know Alexius himself

Afflictions

Imperial Disapproval (1-9 pts): The character has performed some action which has resulted in the Emperor's disfavor. The more significant the action, the higher the bonus for taking this Affliction. Insulting a low-ranking member of the Emperor's court may be considered a five-point Affliction, while insulting the Vau ambassador while representing the Emperor may garner the full 10 points. The player and gamemaster should decide at the time of character creation what sort of action has been performed to result in this Affliction. Taking Imperial Disapproval does not mean that the Emperor is actively seeking to destroy the character or cause her harm; it does, however, mean that she will have a harder time gaining an audience with the Emperor or his representatives than someone who does not possess this Affliction. In addition, her reputation as *persona non grata* in the Emperor's eyes may also affect her relations with anyone hoping to remain in the Emperor's good graces. (Conversely, enemies of the Emperor may see the character as a potential ally — which may cause further problems.)

1 = A low-ranking member of the Imperial court dislikes you

2 = You have earned the dislike of one of the Imperial Guard

3 = You have offended an important member of the Imperial Court

5 = You have insulted one of the Emperor's highest ranking officials or most important ambassadors

7 = A member of the Emperor's immediate family dislikes you

9 = You have managed to anger Alexius himself

Den of Vipers: House Decados

by James Estes

Konrad Decados was not a happy man.

His ship hovered silently near the Dover, their noses almost touching. Oh, how he would love to ready all weapons at the Hawkwood vessel: Lucy Hawkwood had caused trouble for him on more than one occasion. He could always find an alibi, and he was sure that Lucy must have made many enemies on whom the deed could be blamed — just last week she killed young Sergei Decados, whom she insisted opened fire on her with no provocation.

But no, he was here on request of Prince Hyram, and though it took him away from personal business, one never ignored Hyram's request. His uncle did so, once, and because of it he exchanged the Barony of New Krakow for a quaint patch of barren earth on Malignatius. Ah well; live and learn.

And now he sat on the bridge of his own personal ship, awaiting contact from the Dover. He looked around his own bridge, examining the impassive faces of the strangers who had replaced his own loyal crew. Finally he turned to the smug face of the woman standing next to him: Milena Decados, an emissary of Prince Hyram. Probably a Jakovian, he considered. Her eyes shot momentarily in his direction and narrowed. And probably a damned psychic too. But he sat back in his chair, and waited for Milena to dictate what would happen next.

Fifteen minutes later, Lucy Hawkwood walked regally onto the bridge, as though all the Empire were bowed before her. Typical Hawkwood.

"Greetings, Noble cousin," she said, without the slightest bit of irony or condescension, her pale blue eyes looking coolly forward and not even at him.

"What is this...witch... doing here? On my ship? Without my consent?" Konrad turned pointedly at Milena, gesturing madly at Lucy, who stood still and crisp in her Hawkwood uniform.

"Konrad," Milena began, in a cold and professional voice that said quite clearly don't interrupt me, *"you have been drafted by the Jakovian Agency as a liaison. Lucy Hawkwood is a spy for House Decados, and you will be her contact. Be mindful of her requests, but maintain your public enmity. And do not take*

her for granted."

She paused, more for dramatic effect than anything. "Or she will be forced to kill you as she did Sergei, and we will have to draft another liaison."

Lucy winked, and licked her lips. Konrad winced. Perhaps Uncle Ivan's patch of dirt on Malignatius wasn't so bad after all.

Introduction

Let history bear one lesson: never take a Decados at face value. A valuable second lesson might be: if you think you've figured out what a Decados is really up to, you're wrong.

To many in the Known Worlds, Decados are unethical miscreants, indulging mindlessly in their own pleasure while hatching some multifarous plot. The Decados certainly enjoy such characterization — a powerful reputation is a useful tool, after all — but they are more than simply hedonistic conspirators. They are advancing the greatest house in space, one which goes back to Holy Terra itself. The future of House Decados is the future of the Empire, and let nothing stand in its way.

House History

Consider everything — and everyone — a resource. They exist merely to further your goals. Use them for their worth, and abandon them at your discretion. Even your enemies are resources — true wisdom lies in using your enemies so that even your defeat is to your benefit.

— The Ducal Manifesto, maxim 5

Few noble houses can claim as prestigious a lineage as that of House Decados, which traces itself with certainty to a Russian noble family of Holy Terra, and boasts one of the longest and greatest bloodlines to cross the stars. The legitimacy of this claim is open to debate — not that the Decados actually care to engage in such debate — since the

first appearance of the house was nearly one thousand years after the death of the last alleged descendent of the Romanovs in the 20th century. Indeed, it was not until 2818 and the coup on Severus that the Known Worlds heard the name Decados.

The Decados Ascendancy, or the Fall of Gloucester

The planet Severus is a harsh and unwelcome place, first colonized by House Gloucester. Like other houses, Gloucester's fortune rose and fell, until finally Severus was its last holding. Severus was, in truth, little more than a tightly controlled mining colony, and was the source of Gloucester's remaining wealth, as Gloucester's operations routinely extracted petrochemicals and rare minerals for export to other worlds. Gloucester was a minor house, but significant: Prince Davies Gloucester was a very distant cousin to House Hawkwood, and the two houses enjoyed an amicable relationship. In 2817, House Gloucester fell on extremely hard times, and its prince discussed joining Gloucester to Hawkwood, knowing that while his own power and his house's independence would diminish, House Gloucester would at least survive.

When a Hawkwood diplomatic ship made the voyage to Severus in 2818, it was greeted with a broadcast by Duke Antonin Decados, self-proclaimed "scion to an an-

cient and newly reborn lineage" — a man who had previously been the security minister to House Gloucester. At his side stood his brother, Jakob Decados, one-time intelligence minister for House Gloucester.

And at their backs stood their "kinsmen," their lost "brothers and sisters, separated by time and space but now rejoined" — many of them intelligence ministers and security officers for countless other now-defunct houses — united under one banner, the Mantis Banner, and one name: House Decados. Their message was simple: House Gloucester was no more. Davies Gloucester had legally forfeited all properties and holdings to the new house, and killed himself soon after. The few remaining Gloucester nobles were "adopted" by the benevolent House Decados, now charged with maintaining the ancestral Gloucester lands. The stunned Hawkwood delegates were welcomed to pay their respects to the newly ascendant House Decados.

The message was carried through jumpgates from ship to ship, across space. A collective universe took note.

An Ancient Dynasty Reborn

In House Decados' early years, it struggled to make a name for itself and to prove its ancient imperial lineage. The First Regime (the first 20 years of Decados history under Antonin Decados) saw the establishment of new customs, the reclamation of ancient traditions, and the beginnings of what would become the Decados way.

One of the first significant actions in the First Regime was the establishment of the Jakovian Agency, the information and propaganda arm of House Decados, helmed by Jakob Decados; his agents began scouring the Known Worlds, gathering vital bits of information lost or forgotten or secreted away. And the right information — coupled with a timely assassination — could bring a world to ruin.

It was during the First Regime that many of the characteristics of House Decados began: the many eccentricities, the systematic inbreeding, and the penchant for things hidden. Antonin was the progenitor of Decados body alteration: "the flesh is such a weak thing," he remarked after watching one tortured prisoner's skin begin to melt, and soon after he began grafting synthetic skins over his own body. By the time of his death, his entire body was covered in a sheath of experimental skin.

In the house's earliest days, assassins and torturers became more than people of skill and necessity: they were craftsmen, artists, even perfectionists whose skills were often showcased like a sculptor's exhibit. The Mantis League was created, and Decados nobles proudly counted master assassins among their retinue. And it was here that the Decados military and political policies were honed and sharpened, as Decados might reached out and grasped its prey, choking and devouring it.

World after world fell to the Decados, and once greater houses were subsumed by the Decados — or simply disappeared. An army of black-garbed dragoons spread across space, under the banner of the mantis, and the yawning maw of the Decados machine became something to be feared.

Decados nobles were (at best) distrusted, thanks to their voracious political appetites and apparent amorality. And those who followed Antonin Decados' example of eschewing the natural-born body gave credence to the reputation of the Decados bogeyman. From the psychotic Zofia Decados, who regularly bludgeoned serfs with her cybernetic arms (except on those unfortunate days when a hand was replaced with serrated blades) to Iancu Decados, who grafted an artificial exocirculatory system to his body so selchakah plasma could intermingle with his own blood, to Stashko Decados, who proudly displayed his cybernetic bodkin outside his clothing and regularly disrupted inter-house councils displaying his prosthetics — the Decados noble was an icon of freakishness.

Divestiture

The pre-eminence of House Decados was cemented during the Divestiture, when various houses began to ally against the decaying Republic. Ironically, the houses which formed the Ten determined many of their strategic actions based upon information provided by House Decados, but only toward the end was House Decados formally invited to join the alliance. Mika Decados, the Hermaphrodite Prince, gladly accepted.

The earliest to protest the entry of the Decados to this august league of nobles was House Hawkwood, which voiced many bitter assignations about the moral fiber of the Decados, and how they were too dangerous a brood of vipers to allow into the fold.

The various houses entertained some debate on the issue, and agreed to submit the issue to a vote; the Decados sent legates to the houses to persuade them of the merits of Decados participation. When the issue was voted upon, House Hawkwood was the clear minority, and House Decados was offered invitation to join the Ten. Very few of the endorsements were enthusiastic, however, and some historians surmise that Decados persuasion may have amounted to either blackmail or bribery. Regardless, the arrival of special envoy Volya Decados was greeted by the other houses only with silence — a silence broken by the clicking of metal across marble as the mechanical arachnid chassis which replaced her legs skittered across the floor.

And thus Decados forces were among those that arrived at Byzantium Secundus, to crush the Rogue Houses and reclaim the captured world. And Lucretzia Decados, the Decados military envoy, raised her family's banner in the ruins of the presidential palace.

The Rogues Gallery

Was there any truth to the rumors that the Decados helped fund the Rogue Houses in their venture, and provided critical information that allowed them the success which they had? Of course not. But some still suspect that the Decados, through an intricate series of double-blind agents, coordinated much of the Rogue Alliance, both as a means of crushing some minor houses and elevating the status of the Decados.

True, Houses Kossuth, Powell, and Von Ferdinand were among the Rogue Houses, and once they had been allies to the Decados; and sadly, after their downfall, their holdings and wealth had to be administered by the Decados.

Likewise, one of the leaders of the alliance was none other than House Romanov, which claimed descent from the very same Russian Imperial family as House Decados (through the blood of the hemophiliac Alexei) and accused House Decados of a fraudulent heritage. ("Thin-blooded pretenders," the Decados would sniff in disdain as their only reply.) And Lucretzia Decados was allegedly seen shooting Prince Grigori Romanov in the back of the skull during the reclamation of Byzantium Secundus. (The witness later claimed he "erred," and saw someone else.)

But the allegation that the Decados maneuvered the Rogue Alliance into a situation of defeat clearly lacks any foundation.

Or at least any proof.

The Mantis and the Lion: the Decados-Hawkwood Enmity

The roots of the rivalry between Houses Hawkwood and Decados go back centuries, to the very beginnings of House Decados. When Hawkwood emissaries appeared near Severus to continue dealings with the newly-defunct House Gloucester, their refusal to honor Antonin Decados was seen as irritating. It was clear that House Hawkwood would not acknowledge the Decados; but Antonin and his family were true nobles, and refused to let this boorishness stand in the way of peace.

Unfortunately, stubborn House Hawkwood refused to compromise. They brooded among their crags and moors about the demise of their cousins, and they rallied the other noble houses against Antonin for his seeming crimes. Ultimately, their arguments fell on fallow grounds: Antonin could document Davies Gloucester's abdication and forfeiture of his family's rights and wealth. But still the stubborn Hawkwoods would not relent, and still the Decados were forgiving in the face of Hawkwood suspicion.

But after 30 years, the situation became critical and the black-hearted Hawkwoods showed their true colors: Hawkwood legates on the Decados ship the *Alexander* killed Jakob Decados in the very midst of a peace summit, and with his death came the realization of how things were to be between the two houses. A brief war ensued, with a number of small skirmishes in which Decados forces had to defend their territories from the aggressive Hawkwoods, such as at the massacres at Chobor-Zemsky and New Caspian. How many young Decados nobles and innocent serfs suffered and died because of Hawkwood attacks? It was a black day for House Decados, and only intervention from other houses and the Universal Church ended the tragic war: a bitter and fragile peace ensued, one which would ever be tested by Hawkwood antagonism and belligerence.

Ironically, the Hawkwoods now like to forget that House Gloucester ever existed, or had any relationship to them. And they likewise claim that they had no role in the death of Jakob Decados, and with a grand dismissal have forgotten the whole incident.

But the Decados do not forget.

A United Empire

Few houses truly trusted the Decados, but it was clear that these houses needed the mantis-lords. They were chief among houses in terms of information: when it came to determining the pulse of the universe, the Decados, to be sure, were superior.

The Decados and House Alecto were never among the closest of allies — and in fact the Shaw-Cardozo incident only heightened distrust between the two parties — and when Vladimir Alecto began drawing the fragmented worlds of the Republic around him, they were among his greatest critics. The Decados never voted for Vladimir's leadership, but were unable to persuade others to their cause. In fact, the disdain with which the Decados held Vladimir — combined with his apathy toward them — bolstered his image. Here was a man even the Decados could not conquer, and this alone rallied other houses to him.

The Decados led other houses against Vladimir, who was allied with Gesar, the Windsors, and the Van Gelder, all of whom eagerly looked forward to trouncing the Decados. The Decados's league lost to Vladimir's superior forces, and an astonished universe watched Baron Nicolai Decados bow in fealty to Vladimir, offering complete surrender. Soon, however, Vladimir was dead by an unidentified assassin's hand, House Alecto was extinct, the Gesar and Windsors were gone, and the Van Gelder bound to the Decados.

The wise might question whether the Decados really lost, or merely found a more convenient means of victory and ensuring defeat of a number of their opponents. The Ten were now Five, and Decados was among them.

The Emperor Wars

The Decados, true to form, were among the loudest critics of Darius Hawkwood when he made his bid for power. Even those who opposed House Hawkwood were hesitant to side with House Decados.

Still, the Hazat and the Decados were allies in arms, and the battle was fierce, and wholly treacherous. Decados assassins and spies combed the universe, seeking to sever the infant Empire's delicate network — blackmail here, assassination there, extortion, and in some cases even rumored slaughter. For years, it almost seemed as though the Decados would win. But even Decados venom could not subdue the growing Empire, and it ultimately became clear that the black-harnessed soldiers of House Decados were fighting a losing battle.

Perhaps it was true — the Decados could successfully uncoil their forces for a single venomous strike, but were incapable of sustained conflict; the Decados soldiers were cruel, and effective, but lacked discipline. It was clear that they could not bully an entire Empire, and they had lost their edge.

Historians and analysts still discuss the Decados' enigmatic surrender to Alexius. It was obvious why the Decados surrendered (they were on the brink of defeat, after all), but the sudden timing remains curious. Had Decados strategists merely formulated a change in their program? Was this — as seemingly with all of the Decados actions — merely part of an overall, inexplicable plan? And why did Alexius allow the Decados to rejoin the Five with impunity?

No doubt, secrets within secrets. And some secrets may never see the light of the fading suns.

The Present Day

The Decados are now a quiet force in imperial politics. It is rumored that Decados information brokers control information on the Five, even on Emperor Alexius himself, and are waiting for the right opportunity to use their information to finally gain the upper hand. It is certainly possible that the Decados themselves are behind these rumors, subtly and insidiously boosting their image with paranoid fears.

The house has lost much of its clout, and other nobles tend to dismiss Decados nobles as a whole as irrelevant players in Imperial politics. Their age of greatness has passed, and even the Decados must bow to the greater glory of the Imperial Phoenix. More keen critics astutely observe that a Decados can never be judged merely on his appearance, and House Decados will always be a vipers' nest. Whether Salandra Decados's alleged romantic affair with Alexius is part of some greater political intrigue has yet to be discerned: perhaps through her, Alexius can turn Decados venom against the Empire's allies; or perhaps Salandra is herself a toxin, coursing slowly through the Empire toward Alexius' heart.

Ways and Means

Etiquette is like a cloak — it can be gaudy and ostentatious, and it can conceal a dagger.

— *The Ducal Manifesto*, maxim 104

The Decados are ruthless opponents, and equally ruthless allies. Decados internal politics are the epitome of natural selection: truly, only the best survive.

In the course of its history, House Decados has raised three principles above all others. Decados philosophy is a difficult beast, filled with subtleties and complex arguments — or sophistries and oxymorons, its critics charge — but can best be understood by the three tenets first articulated by Antonin and Jakob Decados and reiterated over the ages:

House Decados over all. In all our endeavors, through all our activities, let us never forget: House Decados over all. Every fiber of our being should be directed toward the growth and sustenance of this, our house. Cast aside petty rivalries and remember our common heritage. Without it, we are nothing.

For all things, a reason. We believe in a Pancreator of Economy; nothing was created that serves no purpose. It is wise to understand a thing's purpose, and it glorifies our Maker to use a thing to its best purpose. Our purpose is clear: it is to serve our house. But all things have such a purpose — in some, to greater a degree than in others — and we do well to consider such at all times.

The ends justify the means. If one acts for the best of reasons, and with the truest and most well-considered of

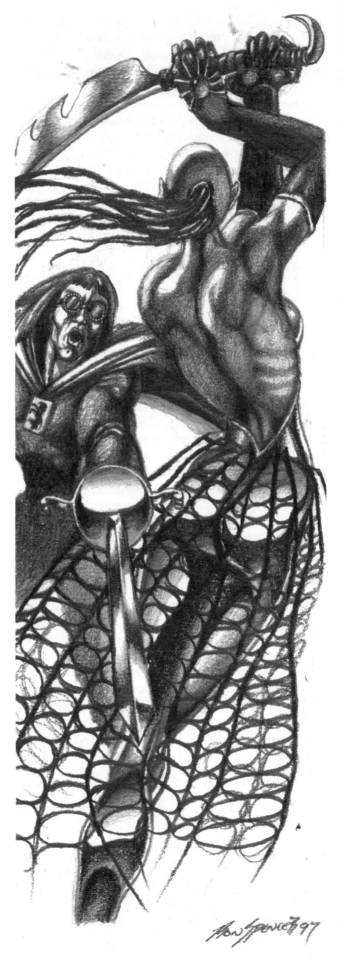

means, then all other considerations fall aside. The fulfillment of a glorious destiny is reason enough to forsake petty convention. For in reaching this grand destiny, all shall benefit, and the sufferings of a few are paltry compared to the joys of all humanity.

These three tenets have spawned centuries of depredation. Opponents of the Decados claim that with these three maxims, the Decados have absolutely rationalized their selfishness: "House Decados over all" is a rallying call for the Decados to reign supreme over all the Known Worlds; "For all things a reason" is the heart of Decados exploitation of natural goods and people; "The ends justify the means" is the reasoning used to justify any Decados action, no matter how heinous.

The Well-Dressed Noble

Decados nobles are expected to adhere to a uniform code of dress: form-fitting black material adorned with the house's mantis symbol. Beyond this template, however, some degree of variety is allowed. The uniform's material may vary depending upon the climate, though most nobles tend to prefer leather (from any variety of beasts), or stiffsynth if available. Likewise, the mantis-symbol may vary in placement, size, or material, from a belt-buckle to a shoulder-patch. Other touches, from the number of belt straps to the shape of buckles, make each uniform truly individual — a paradox which the vain and clannish Decados are proud of.

Few Decados truly live up to the image of the inhuman freak which has become their house's stereotype. Certainly most Decados nobles value individuality and experimentation, and are more likely to engage in body alteration than most nobles — but this is typically limited to the occasional prosthetic or pigment change. (Incidentally, sometimes a unique feature is the result of an ancestor who dabbled in genetic modification.) Only rarely is a Decados likely to reach the excesses of Prince Demeter Decados, whose fingers were replaced with a dozen synthetic digits resembling tentacles and whose massive tattooed torso was sustained by a hovering platform that uncontrollably discharged liquid body waste and engine oil with unsettling frequency.

As a last note — always remember, when seeing a seemingly-unarmed Decados: there is no such thing as an unarmed Decados.

A Noble's Upbringing

A Decados's career begins the moment she is born. Sickly or weak children are often abandoned at birth; a weak infant could only make a weak adult, incapable of serving House Decados. Most such infants are simply killed, while a few manage to be shipped offworld and raised as foster children, disinherited by House Decados and ignorant of their heritage, or sold to slavers.

Tutelage

Decados ethics are instilled in their children at an early age. Part of this training is systematic, with young children adopting a uniquely Decados way of perceiving the Known Worlds and their inhabitants as resources. Part of this training is experiential; only the craftiest children can thrive in the back-biting Decados society, and one learns to adapt, or suffer.

Strong children are taken from their parents and put into the care of a tutor, who raises the children and instructs them in the ways of House Decados. Young nobles learn early the importance of their role in house (and Imperial) politics, and loyalty to the Mantis banner is deeply ingrained.

Decados tutelage, always overseen by the Jakovian Agency, varies from tutor to tutor. Some tutors may deal with only a certain age range, while other tutors may instruct a child for the better part of its life. Likewise, some tutors may select only one child at a time, while others instruct small groups. In some cases, the tutor lives with the child and her family, but more often raises the child apart from her parents.

Young Decados are often raised away from their parents for a reason: Decados philosophers believe in loyalty to House Decados, not to one's actual sires. This avoids more clannish behavior within the house itself, and has proven successful to some degree — more than one Decados child has furthered his own career through betrayal of a disloyal sire or sibling.

As soon as the child is able, she is taught the arts of war — from the necessities of self-defense to the basic principles of assassination, from the duel to the arts of the vendetta. Training varies, so that some young nobles may learn Jox Boxing (Ur-Ukar hand-to-hand fighting) or another martial art, while others might concentrate more on weaponry. Concurrently with this martial training, a Decados child learns the art of passive espionage. Information is everywhere, waiting to be gleaned from even the simplest conversation. One need only learn to be aware at all times, and fully focused when interacting with people.

The Adult Decados

At age 18 (sometimes earlier) the young Decados is considered an adult and leaves his tutor to become a fullfledged *boyar*, or knight. The young boyar almost always enters Decados service — otherwise he is denied the right of inheritance. Some boyars choose to wander the Known Worlds, living on a family stipend while learning more about the Empire — but such service is almost always inevitable.

House Decados has many roles for young nobles to fill, from governmental minister to diplomatic legate to military officer. After four years of service, nobles are eligible for inheritance. Some nobles choose to continue serving their house, making it a lifelong career for them. Others, desiring neither the burden of land management or the responsibilities of governance, roam the stars instead, seeking their own destiny.

Decados Peerage

Decados titles are hereditary, but not absolute — they depend upon serving House Decados and the whim of the Prince himself. For instance, the heir to the Duchy of New Archangel must first serve a tour of duty in either the Decados government or military or his inheritance is forfeit; or Prince Hyram may reward a pleasing sycophant with the Duchy of New Archangel, regardless of inheritance rights or who currently owns it. A Decados noble bereft of his inheritance may retain his title, but it is a memento at best, and a painful sting of dishonor at worse.

The Prince, of course, is a single individual, whom all must obey in any matter, at any cost. For now, he (or she) is the apex of the Decados hierarchy; but the Decados have long dreamed that one of their own would hold sway over all of the Known Worlds, as the first Decados Tsar.

The Vendetta

The art of dueling is eclipsed among the Decados by the vendetta, an ancient tradition with prescribed guidelines, which is a viable tool of political domination within the house. It may be as minor as defending one's honor against an alleged affront — but for the Decados, it can also be a means of public declaration of war against a fellow Decados.

It is through the vendetta that the Decados war with each other, as a clash of will and wit which may never need resort to steel. The rules of engagement are clear: both participants must agree upon the terms, and Decados resources must never be expended to satisfy a personal insult. What might have been an all-out attack on a fellow Decados's household — resulting in a loss of resources better used serving the house proper — becomes instead a managed conflict with minimal loss. The terms vary from vendetta to vendetta, and must be approved and overseen by a Decados noble litigator known as the Master Jurist. In this regard, a vendetta can last from minutes to years, and the antagonists can fight each other with swords, prove one's superiority in marksmanship, or hire assassins against each other — whomever can prove himself better at the agreed-upon technique is clearly the victor, and the actual method itself is often irrelevant.

Decados nobles never engage non-Decados nobles (something of an oxymoron, the high-minded Decados comment) with a vendetta, which is clearly the mark of true culture. They will duel nobles of other houses, and are prone to what other houses decry as cheating, but which Decados see merely as "resourceful behavior."

La Dolce Vita
Gossip

Information is the currency with which one can buy the Republic.
— *The Ducal Manifesto*, maxim 12

What many houses see as merely "gossip," the Decados more clearly understand as necessary communication.

The early founders of House Decados agreed on one thing: information is power. What was often little more than a 20th-century adage has become a pivotal concept in Decados negotiations.

Decados representatives deal with many resources — fuel, rare minerals, technology, and all the various resources commonly bartered across space. None are considered as precious as information, however: key bits of information, particularly contraband or long-lost knowledge, may be dealt with as pure currency by House Decados.

Gossip is merely an informal means of brokering information for a skilled Decados. Many Decados are trained conversationalists, not merely to seem glib and witty but to subtly direct a conversation. "Beware a chatty Decados" is time-worn wisdom, oft-ignored by a fool-hardy (and inebriated) noble who learns, too late, how much information he has unknowingly volunteered.

Revelry

The Decados have perfected the social engagement, and are capable of anything from a light tête-à-tête to a full-fledged bacchanalia. But these are far more than merely soirees; they are a means of exchanging and acquiring information. Certain Decados events are held only for members of the household, but the more grand and elaborate events are open to guests from across the Known Worlds — after all, what good is putting on a show with only the showmen to see it?

Among the most cautiously anticipated Decados events is the Grand Masquerade, held annually on Severus and sponsored by Prince Hyram himself. Attended by the cream of Decados culture, its guests are prominent individuals from all the Known Worlds. Many guests come and go throughout the evening, and rumors run rampant as to who is truly behind which mask: costumes are believed to change hands throughout the night. The vital — and otherwise classified — information pried from drunken lips at this event is unsurprising; what is surprising is how many people still willingly attend the event, led like gaily-bedecked lambs to a rather festive slaughter.

Athletes

Decados nobles are fond of athletics — watching them, that is — and are most fond of what they call simply "The Games": a series of contests that amount to little more than gladiatorial matches.

The variety of these contests is almost endless. Contestants might simply be thrown into a cage and told to fight, put on an obstacle course and told to evade pursuit, and so on. Likewise, contestants might fight individually, in pairs or teams, or even in a large free-for-all. These athletic contests are popular with the nobility, who regularly sponsor games or wager on the success of various athletes.

Athletic programs are sponsored by nobles who pay for the training and lodging of their prized athletes. Decados athletes are not slaves — but once entering a noble's athletic program (one to three years of service), they have no option in what events they will participate. Still, their training and pay are enviable, and athletes often take their skills to the private sector, acting as mercenary bodyguards or bounty hunters. Decados athletics are an equal-opportunity program, open to anyone: even known criminals are accepted into the program, given a provisional pardon for the duration of their service, and given full pardon should they reach champion level.

The Katerina Run is the most notorious of the games, for it is set on an abandoned Vau spaceship found in the Cadiz system. This game is held once every three years and is among the most challenging (and eagerly anticipated) of the games. The Katerina Run is, in fact, open to anyone who would enter, for the prize is generous: 10,000 firebirds for the winning team, full pardon for any crimes (at least on Decados worlds; crimes against the Empire are another story), and freedom for serfs. Teams are placed in strategic locations on the ship and given a time limit in which they have to reach a specific on-board site — a task not easily done, as the odds are stacked quite heavily against participants, from competition among contestants to automated defenses and more. Indeed, the ship itself has yet to be fully explored, and its operations are still largely incomprehensible to its Decados owners. The Decados patron of the event was once nearly killed when a serf contestant returned to the bridge with a bizarre energy weapon he'd found in a locker. Only the serf's own ineptitude with the weapon saved the lord, whose cybernetic life support kept him alive as everybody else in the room was sucked out of the hull breach which the weapon had made.

Relations

Cultivate allies, control accomplices, subjugate inferiors, avoid witnesses.
— *The Ducal Manifesto*, maxim 37

Noble Houses

House Hawkwood: The Decados's strongest rivalry to date is with House Hawkwood, which currently holds the strongest position of favor in the Emperor's eye. This deepseated rivalry began well before the Emperor Wars; now they are forced to be friendly, but neither party trusts the other. A bitter river flows between these two houses, and the Decados relish every defeat the Hawkwoods face — some say that behind every Hawkwood defeat can be found a Decados scheme, and rumors whispered in agorae across space hint at fierce retribution coming to House Hawkwood.

House Keddah: In time, this house of honor-bound altruists will expire, and their planet Grail, rich with resources, will belong entirely to the Decados. After all, who better to shepherd the assets of House Keddah than the Decados, who have so graciously looked after this minor house's needs?

House Van Gelder: This house of assassins is a useful ally to House Decados; but Decados nobles are ever watchful that the Van Gelder's teeth might be turned against the Mantis. Should that ever happen, then this little house shall have to become more familiar with the Jakovian kossacks.

House Masseri: The Decados conquered this house of fur traders, allowing them to manage an estate on Cadavus, and thinks of them as little more than Decados freemen. In time, their weak blood will die out.

The Universal Church

House Decados maintains a precarious relationship with the Church. The house certainly pays lip-service to the Church, funding the construction of enormous cathedrals on Decados worlds, and appointing Orthodox priests as advisors.

But in reality the "spiritual advisors" have no authority, and religion in general is something the house could do without. Given the opportunity, the Decados would probably rather see the Church driven to the ground in order to end their constant fanatical interference. However, the house must be respectful in its dealings with the Church, for it is a powerful entity, and the Decados understand power.

Eskatonic Order: House Decados has been historically suspicious of the wandering mystics of the Eskatonic Order. Perhaps the Eskatonics are able to see through the layers of deception and the many masks that a Decados wears, and can unmask one with frightening ease — at least, this is what Eskatonic priests believe. House Decados counters that these meddling Rasputins only stir up trouble.

Temple Avesti: Many Decados nobles act in manners best identified as deviant, and rumors constantly surface about Decados Antinomism. However, the house has managed to avoid major investigation from the Inquisition, and some suspect that the Decados know something the Avestites would rather not have revealed. If this is so, both Temple Avesti and the Decados must tread carefully — the relationship between the two is fragile, if not downright volatile.

The Merchant League

Decados nobles have a cordial rivalry with the Merchant League. The Decados know that the League provides services and goods which the Decados need, and can

no longer control. In this respect, the League has actually earned some respect — after all, the guilds are successful and, in a sense, the fulfillment of the Decados "survival of the fittest" ethic. On the other hand, if given the opportunity, the Decados would crush the League beneath their heel and subjugate it as yet another resource. The League recognizes this, and is ever on guard around Decados nobles.

Engineers: House Decados has a strained relationship with the Supreme Order, who now control a business which the Decados once excelled in: body manipulation, from genetic engineering to flesh grafting and cybernetics. Where once Decados was the master, it is now the client — a position which Decados nobles abhor. The Genetechs Cartel (see below), designed to be a compromise, both contains and heightens the dispute.

The Muster (Chainers): Decados nobles have frequent dealings with the Chainers, who provide additional laborers for many Decados projects. Whether these laborers are paid or slaves all depends upon whom you ask and how honest an answer you expect. Both Decados and Chainers deny that their transactions smack of any wrongdoing, but Decados and Chainer alike frequently deny many things.

Aliens

Aliens are, like everything else to the Decados, a resource. The Ur-Ukar are sometimes contracted by individual Decados nobles for their personal retinue, but the house as a whole is uncomfortable about letting these violent aliens too close. The Decados disdain — which often means "fear" — the Vorox, who are simply too unruly to control, and are thus useless.

Ascorbites: This carapaced humanoid race is native to Severus, the Decados homeworld. Before the fall of House Gloucester, the Ascorbites were already subjugated and terrorized into servitude. The Decados made the situation for Ascorbites even worse, and consider them to have little more intelligence than dogs, but of innately less value — dogs are far better looking and easier to train, after all.

Holdings

The worlds are trophies to your excellence.
— The Ducal Manifesto, maxim 198

The Decados prize their holdings — the people and the planets under their thumb — for both their own intrinsic merit and for their cumulative value: the ancient Terran phrase, "the one with the most toys wins," was surely conceived with the Decados in mind.

Worlds

Primary among the Decados holdings are its planets. Sadly, House Decados has fewer planets in its grasp now than it once did — during the Dark Ages some planets sealed themselves off from the Known Worlds. And the majority of their worlds are now mere shells, having been sucked dry of almost all resources.

Severus

The jungle planet Severus is the homeworld of the Decados — and some would say that a more fitting place could not exist. It is a harsh, treacherous planet with dangers lurking everywhere. The flora and fauna of Severus can be beautiful, almost intoxicating — but just as often it may be carnivorous and simply fatal. The similarity between the Severan *buorka*-flower, with its brilliantly colored and beautiful petals but painfully toxic oil, and the effete and treacherous Decados nobles is not easily dismissed.

Despite the many hardships associated with Severus (especially the Severan hull rats), many call Severus home. Mining for rare trace-minerals still takes place, but most Severan residents are not miners — they are refugees and expatriates (called elsewhere "criminals") from the rest of the Empire, offered sanctuary at Severus in exchange for loyalty to House Decados. Now these upstanding citizens support every facet of life on Severus, from farming to merchantry. Some continue the activities which led them to flee their homeworlds (assassination, black marketing, drug trafficking, etc.), but, provided these services are rendered for House Decados and not against it, there is little problem from the local lords.

Hyram Decados maintains Manse Decados, the ducal palace for the entire house; he resides here with his entourage and many supporters, running House Decados with a tight fist.

Edenya: Severus has a small moon which, like itself, is covered by jungle. Edenya is inhabitable, but only barely so. Flora and fauna are equally venomous, and a cloying haze of humidity makes the already acrid air difficult to breathe. Edenya is owned and run by the Jakovian Agency; all that the public knows is that the kossack training camp is on Edenya, and everything else is classified. The Jakovians monitor all entry and egress to Edenya.

Malignatius

The arctic planet Malignatius is something of an anomaly among Decados holdings: nowhere else among the Decados does such religious fervor run through the populace. The variance in sects and beliefs that regularly crop up and disappear on Malignatius lead viewers to one observation: it doesn't matter what the religion is, the Malignatians are simply, innately religious. Take any religion away from them and another will take its place.

This of course vexes the Church, but it amuses the Decados. The planet has developed something of an unfortunate reputation among Decados nobles; incurring Prince Hyram's wrath could lead you to exile on Malignatius (assuming it does not lead you to death), and for some unfortunates, this has become a cold and bitter prison.

A number of gulags have been established on Malignatius for Decados dissidents and troublemakers. Their lives are often short. The frozen wastes of this planet are also homes to number of monastics — some members of the Universal Church, and others claiming no religious affiliation whatsoever — who spend their days in quiet isolation, meditating and studying texts often believed lost to time.

Julka: Malignatius's single moon is even more inhospitable than Malignatius. Julka is the setting of a large, heavily protected subterranean gulag, where the house's most notorious criminals go. There is no escape.

Cadiz

Cadiz is an enigma — massively built up with metropoli for the Known Worlds elite, it is now an enormous tenement. The Second Republic had chosen this planet for diplomatic negotiations with the Vau, and,

---

Selchakah

Among Severus' most popular — and equally contraband — exports is the Severan opiate poppy, which produces *selchakah*: an extremely addictive narcotic which is usually illegal outside of Decados holdings.

Selchakah takes its users to the seat of joy, and offers a form of painless bliss — extreme but fleeting at first, then dwindling to an hours-long period of dreamy tranquillity. Lower grade selchakah offers at least a period of painlessness and the illusion of happiness. Higher grades of the drug provide moments of such beatific bliss and clarity that they have been compared with epiphanies of the Pancreator. Selchakah has sometimes been called Sathra-root, for it can alleviate addiction to the Sathra experience. But Selchakah is addictive: at first users can go weeks, even months between doses, but eventually the doses become closer and closer, and few addicts can go more than two days without a dose.

The drug is a serious point of contention among the Known Worlds: most noble houses have declared it illegal, the League officially refuses to carry it, and the Church inveighs against selchakah for its neo-Sathraist tendencies. Decados smugglers, of course, run a lucrative business of carrying the contraband drug to spaceports across the Empire, even to Byzantium Secundus itself.

The extremes to which a selchakah addict will go to replenish his stock range from the mundane to legendary, including murder and high treason. The fact that selchakah addicts have been found among the nobles of all the houses has frightening implications — how many state secrets have been exchanged for a week's worth of the drug?

One dose of the drug costs three firebirds (more where the seller risks imminent danger selling it).

---

along with the Decados, poured money and labor into building and beautifying the cities that covered this planet. When the Vau chose another site, the Decados were disgusted, and abruptly ceased their construction efforts, leaving many partially-finished structures in place — structures which now house the poor and starving occupants of the planet. The cities of Cadiz are now known as harbors for activity illegal among Decados planets, for the house seems to have abandoned the world. Decados dragoons do sporadically sweep the planet in security searches.

Cadiz is also home to the Hironem, the reptilian natives of the now-conquered world. The Hironem live on a reservation, at the center of which is Turaz, their capital city. Scholars from across the Known Worlds come to Turaz (for a hefty fee, of course) to study Hironem culture and ways, which bears a few distinct similarities to Vau culture.

Persus: Due to its toxic atmosphere, Cadiz' sole moon is uninhabitable, except for a controlled-atmosphere military base. The base acts as a giant dockyard for old Decados ships, either for repairs or scavenging. Ruins of an unidentified culture exist on the dark side of Persus, with entrances to sublunar caverns. But this entire region is cordoned off by the Decados, with entry forbidden to all except by Prince Hyram's personal request.

Cadavus

The Decados are blessed with possession of Cadavus, arguably the poorest planet in the Empire. Decados forces seized Cadavus during the Emperor Wars, seeking a cell of anti-Decados terrorists, and no one wanted the planet back. In time, the house began to wonder why it kept the planet, because its resources are almost depleted. Still, the Decados obviously have something to eke out of the planet, or they would have abandoned it long ago.

Cadavus also has the distinction of having been home to almost every known (and maybe even unknown) faction within the Empire. Prior to Decados rulership, it was owned by the Merchant League, which had used it as a major shipping port — a remnant from the days when Cadavus still had resources and reasons for ships to stop there.

The most visible reminder of previous ownership is seen in the proliferation of monasteries that dot the surface. Representatives of almost every religious group, major and minor, can be found here, and rumors of a Sathraist monastery still persist. Some of these monasteries date back to the planet's early colonization, and their records are filled with rich details about the history of spacefaring, bringing many scholars to the planet.

There is a Xanthippe Moonhaven on the largest of Cadavus's two moons.

Pandemonium

Pandemonium is a Decados frontier world, and is fully described in the **Fading Suns** rulebook. Activity on Pandemonium has heightened considerably with the discovery of Iver, and Decados fleet activity has increased in the vicinity. House Decados is split on the best course of action — whether to simply send in dragoons — and kossacks if need be — to claim the world which they believe is rightfully Decados, or whether to attempt a more subtle and steady takeover.

Grange Station: Of equal importance near Pandemonium is the uncompleted jumpgate contested by House Decados and the Charioteers. Count Enis Sharn arranged for a marginally functional Second Republic starbase, originally in orbit around Pandemonium, to be towed near the uncompleted jumpgate — to plant the Decados banner near the jumpgate.

Unfortunately, his plan has backfired. The Emperor has decided that "Grange Station" would be an excellent exercise in cooperation, and has called for the station to be jointly staffed by the League and House Decados, collaborating to discover the secrets of the jumpgate, and overseen by an Imperial monitor to maintain the peace (unfortunately, he has no ability to enforce his suggestions). Whether this forced compromise is merely a farce which will exacerbate the tension has yet to be proven.

Grange Station is an old Second Republic monitoring station, capable of housing nearly 500 people. All but the largest ships can dock at any of its five working bays, and shuttlecraft can dock at its numerous small bays. It is marginally operative, with Engineers constantly trying to revive failing Second Republic systems and repair its decaying superstructure. Glyphs of unknown origin have been found in one recently discovered access tunnel, which some people believe have Sathraist origins.

People

Your forces are like your dress saber: both must be polished, and ready to cut an enemy down without notice. A little flourish is nice — a sharp blade, better.
— *The Ducal Manifesto*, maxim 83

House Decados has a variety of services at its disposal. Where Decados nobles have a reputation for being merely devious, those who work for the Decados are universally respected for the quality of their work — if not exactly for its virtue.

Jakovian Agency

Information is power, as the old adage would have it.

The Jakovian Agency is the seat of such power in House Decados, and is one of the oldest organizations in Decados history, in fact tracing back to Jakob Decados, the first Minister of Intelligence for House Decados for some 30 years until his murder by Hawkwood extremists. The agency which he organized and ran is responsible for the

flow of information into, out of, and throughout the entire house, and is ruthless in the enforcement of its task. It controls all philosophical, scientific ventures that occur within House Decados, and supervises education and propaganda efforts.

Interrogation

The Jakovians manage all interrogation for the house, and Jakovian torturers are among the most skilled and talented in the Known Worlds. For them, talent counts; torture is an art, a talent to be perfected. Just as only the most talented painter can work with canvas and oils to bring about the desired feelings in a painting's audience, so can only a talented torturer bring about the desired results with the tools of flesh, fire, and iron.

Jakovian torture is made up of many diverse methods, from psychological to psychic to physical. Jakovian torturers take an inhuman delight in their tasks, and are constantly experimenting and refining their art. Prisoners who are given to the Agency for physical torture rarely survive: only the strongest can outlast the torture for any length, but inevitably the desired information comes — often with a torrent of blood and tears.

Apprentice torturers begin their training by watching master torturers at work; they then practice on laborers deemed ineffective, or on lesser quality slaves purchased in bulk from the Chainers.

Espionage

The Jakovian Agency acts as House Decados' espionage unit. Its spies have the reputation for being the most talented infiltrators among the Known Worlds — not that anyone can actually identify who is a spy for the Agency. Information smugglers are relatively well-known and highly sought after, but they must rely upon the clandestine chain of unknown agents who provide this ill-gotten information to begin with.

Some fear that in truth, the Jakovian Agency answers to no one, and what happened to House Gloucester could happen once more if the Decados elite are not wise.

The Kossacks

Kossacks are the strong-arm of the Jakovian agency, and will storm in by force to accomplish what intrigue, seduction or cajoling cannot. Those who would be kossacks must attend a rigorous training program which teaches the art of cruelty and subjugation to the highest degree. Indeed, a kossack is no longer human by some sects' definitions, counted instead among the Changed (genetically altered).

A single kossack soldier is said to be the equivalent of any ten men, and a unit of ten kossacks is more than enough to take out an entire squadron of soldiers. Perhaps this is hyperbole, but it speaks of a very telling truth: the kossacks are dangerous foes. Their own life means nothing to them in the line of service, and far more kossacks die in the line of duty than retire. Retirement

---

---

has its privileges, of course — serfs who survive their tour of duty receive freedom and even knighthood in some cases, and those few survivors can command a high price as mercenary soldiers. Decados noble kossacks are among the most persistent and dangerous of individuals, oftentimes feared by their own peers.

Kossacks are incredibly loyal to their own leaders and to House Decados, but anyone they consider beneath them or obstacles to the completion of their goal — even if they be nobles — are treated with contempt. In this respect, kossacks have tremendous leeway among the Decados. Too much leeway, some say: the kossacks are perfectly capable of wiping out their own house, if they unite to do so; many critics believe that the leash which holds taut the kossacks is already weak and fraying.

· **Training** — Jakovian kossacks are typically selected from the ranks of the Decados army, and are noble and serf alike.

They endure physical training unlike that of any other military service: kossack recruits are forced to survive in a harsh living environment on Edenya (Severus's moon), with only remedial medical care. Their physical training is complemented by psychological indoctrination and periods of submersion in chemical baths ("Think Tanks") which ultimately transform the kossack into a strong brute capable of enduring almost endless pain and withstanding psionic manipulation.

This regimen is cruel and completely inhuman, and recruits often have negative reactions to the drugs. The program has a 40% drop-out rate, in addition to a 23% fatality rate.

· **Livery** — A Jakovian kossack is unmistakable, in his sculpted plastic half-plate black armor with its striated musculature, his featureless face mask (which acts both to intimidate and also filter out toxins) and heavy black cloak. His weapons are the finest quality, from Van Gelder assault rifles to hand-crafted sabers.

The Military

Decados soldiers have a reputation for ruthlessness, brutality, and dirty fighting. If you want a career soldier, go to the Hazat; if you want a career terrorist, go to the Decados. The mere presence of Decados dragoons is usually more than sufficient to quiet an unruly mob.

Anyone living in Decados holdings has the opportunity to enlist in the Decados military; despite the many hardships associated with it, many serfs still try to qualify for the military — it offers poor youth a chance of freedom from a lifetime of almost indentured servitude. However, this freedom is not without cost: in exchange for salary and a career, the youth undergoes harsh training and indoctrination. Earn a uniform, lose a soul.

The Decados military handles many tasks — from planetary security and defense to basic police patrol. Few soldiers have the seniority and cache of choosing assignments, and must simply accept the postings doled out by Decados officers.

The chain of command in the Decados military is simple: obey your commanding noble officer. Disobedience is punishable at the officer's discretion. There are no courts to oversee noblemen or how they command enlistees: such sentimental tomfoolery has no place in a true army. Decados officers "killed in the line of fire" are not a rarity — but few soldiers would risk the unforgiving penalty levied on enlistees believed of killing an officer.

Cartels

Decados cartels are something of a marriage between government and industry: they are associations of craftsmen who act not under the Merchant League but through Decados patronage, and are required by contract to serve House Decados exclusively.

In the days before the Merchant League, there were many more cartels. With the formation of the League, however, most Decados cartels simply became absorbed into larger non-Decados guilds. But a few cartels remained, though they are now nothing more than businessmen who receive Decados patronage and governance. The Merchant League has repeatedly attempted to seduce the various remaining cartels into abandoning their Decados patrons, but to no avail.

The Mantis League

The Mantis League was the first cartel formed exclusively for Decados clientele. When a Decados vendetta called for assassins, the rules of engagement required that a neutral third party provide assassins; hence the Mantis League was created, at first simply to provide knowledgeable cartel-licensed killers who could and would observe all rules of engagement. In time, however, the Mantis League's assassins were hired for purposes other than the vendetta, and eventually, Mantis assassins were available for hire outside House Decados. The Mantis League had a very profitable trade.

When the Decados made peace with Prince Alexius, they were forced to officially restrict the Mantis League, so that it could no longer be hired outside House Decados or for any purpose other than enforcing Decados vendettas: Alexius even argued for the dissolution of the Mantis League, but on that Prince Hyram would not budge: "Our traditions are sacred." Hyram now boasts that the Known Worlds need no longer fear the Mantis League. No one believes him, but he boasts it anyway.

Genetechs

The Genetechs are unique among Decados cartels, for they are the only group allied with the Merchant League yet still part of House Decados.

The Genetechs began as a guild of surgeons and scientists who specialized in genetic manipulation with the goal of body modification — literally rewriting a body's genetic code — dedicated totally to House Decados. When negotiations between the nobles and the Merchant League began, the existence of the Genetechs (whose services provided direct competition with the Engineers) proved an almost insurmountable obstacle for Decados-League relations.

Eventually, a solution was devised: the Genetechs would merge with the Engineers, but House Decados would pay the guild for exclusive service by the Genetechs. Discoveries and new creations from the Genetechs would be offered solely to House Decados, and were not required to be shared with the Engineers' Guild at large. This has caused considerable frustration for the Engineers, but they have mastered the art of retaliation by delaying repairs or supplies to Genetech labs and sometimes withholding important news from the Genetechs, forcing a quid pro quo exchange of information. The existence of the cartel is still troubling to many Engineers, who argue against this exclusivity of service; likewise, House Decados is irked by the fact that it must pay the guild anything at all.

The Genetechs are masters of bodily manipulation on the genetic level as well as through cybernetic enhancement. This is more than just cosmetic surgery (although the Genetechs Cartel provides that, too). Want to change from an ectomorph to an endomorph? Desire different skin pigmentation? Looking for the latest adrenal stimulator node? The Genetechs Cartel is the place to go. But prices are incredibly steep, and few but the richest can afford its services.

Rumors indicate that the Jakovian Agents are among the cartel's most frequent customers; the implications of the cartel's services, and how they can be of value to the Jakovian's espionage agents, go without saying.

Serfdom

By far, the majority of people in Decados states are serfs, whom the Decados nobles treat little differently than the raw resources with which the laborers must work. The role of serf is simple: he is a worker, with only limited rights. Serfs are more than simply agriculturists in the Decados society: they are the gears that run the Decados engine. They build the monuments and palaces which glorify House Decados, they till the fields and mine the raw minerals from the earth, and work in often inhumane working conditions to provide the Decados with the material goods a noble requires.

Being a worker in a Decados world is a harsh and unforgiving lot, one which many try to escape by hooking up with one of guilds of the Merchant League. Amaltheans often protest Decados management techniques, which turn workplaces into workcamps, but for now, there is no end in sight. Decados intellectuals remain unpersuaded by this rhetoric, for they believe that Decados laborers must be taxed to the extreme of their abilities, that they might better benefit from knowing that they are fulfilling their own destinies.

The Fleet

House Decados once had an impressive line of starships, but many were either decimated during the Emperor Wars or decommissioned immediately afterward.

Still, the house retains more ships than other houses are happy with (particularly the Hawkwoods), and possibly more are in hiding.

The flagship of the fleet is the *Nicholas and Alexandra*, a cruiser regularly stationed in orbit around Severus. It serves as the personal ship for Prince Hyram, when he makes his few travels from the Decados homeworld to Byzantium Secundus or to other Decados worlds.

The *Nicholas and Alexandra* has a sister-ship, the *Alexis*, which frequently travels in the unknown territories of barbarian space in search of forgotten jumpgates or previously undiscovered worlds. Hyram Decados denies that the *Alexis* is merely a military dreadnought disguised as an exploration ship, but only a fool would travel into barbarian space unarmed — and the Decados are hardly fools.

The remainder of the Decados fleet is a variety of ships, from luxury liners to single pilot fighters. Every ship owned by a Decados citizen is automatically registered with the Decados military, and is subject to conscription for military purposes in times of war.

Personages

Immorality and immortality are synonyms. Virtue is the surest obstacle to longevity.
— *The Ducal Manifesto*, maxim 39

Hyram Decados

Prince Hyram Decados has ruled his house for over 30 years, yet he has now apparently turned away from Imperial politics — to the astonishment of many — in favor of deep space exploration. No doubt he still keeps a steady eye on the doings of his many enemies, but something must have come to his attention that would make him personally interested in unknown space.

Hyram is an enormous man fond of body piercings and bare flesh: he would be crippled, thanks to a would-be assassin's bullet which severed his spinal cord, but the cybernetic legs which support his massive upper body allow him some measure of mobility. He does not often reveal these spindly constructs — an unusual act of modesty for a Decados — typically wrapping his lower body in rich cloths. He is a man fond of displaying his opulence, with many-jeweled rings on all his fingers. But he has certainly mellowed with age: he no longer hosts debaucheries on holy days, and he has discussed dismantling the Eunuch League, the Prince's historic personal servants, whose gossamer kilts do little to conceal their scars — which often causes distress for visiting nobles and

Churchmen.

Hyram's own supporters consider him a manipulative, iron-fisted despot. However, in this respect he continues a long line of Decados despots, and the House is fully used to such behavior — the Prince must be the epitome of the Decados way. Hyram is doubtless one of the least-trusted and most universally-despised men in the Known Worlds.

Some Decados believe that Hyram is to blame for losing the Emperor Wars and shall bring his house to ruin; others believe that their Prince has a proverbial ace up his sleeve. Only time will tell.

Natasha Decados

Natasha Decados's whereabouts are a mystery, but Prince Hyram's niece and her network of supporters have earned intergalactic attention in their attempts to thwart Decados expansion and reveal Decados treacheries.

Natasha was raised in the Prince's own household, her parents having been killed for treason just after her birth. She was an excellent student, mastering unarmed combat and a variety of weapons as well as demonstrating a keen mind, but she was highly critical of the Decados way; it was only because of her great promise as a leader, warrior, and strategist that she was not exiled. In time she quieted, and it was assumed that she had embraced her heritage. She served as a diplomat on Byzantium Secundus, and some believe she was a Jakovian spy.

She disappeared en route to Severus, and at first House Hawkwood was blamed — but her house soon learned that she was in hiding, and actively working against her own family. It is feared exactly how much she knows and how much damage she could do, and Decados citizens are under orders to take her alive at all costs.

Grigori Decados

The favored son of Hyram, Grigori stands ready to inherit the mantle of Prince and rule the Decados holdings. He is a handsome youth — so handsome that many wonder whether he could truly be Hyram's son — with alabaster skin and amethyst eyes, both gifts of Genetech engineering. Other than a mane of ebony hair, he seems completely hairless. He follows his father's custom of going bare-chested, though he often wears a short velvet cloak secured over one shoulder to a nipple-ring. Grigori's only known cybernetic modification is a sleek and glistening left forearm, typically terminated in a functioning hand but occasionally ending in a whirring multibladed instrument.

Grigori is an enigma to many, even among the Decados. His motivations are utterly inscrutable; of course, this might merely be an indication of the success with which Grigori carries out plots and machinations. He is Decados, after all, and few doubt that Hyram would favor a son he considers unworthy of the princely title, and incapable of holding together the vain and arrogant Decados nobility.

Some whisper that Grigori is in fact the son of Andrei Decados, Prince Hyram's missing younger brother — the self-styled Collector of Pain, whose exploits made him legendary across the Known Worlds. But these same whispers also hint that Andrei covertly communicates with Grigori, and that young Grigori has reopened Andrei's Pain Studio beneath Manse Decados. More than one advisor has learned never to discuss these rumors around Hyram, however, who has flown into a rage at their utterance.

Although he owns his own estate on Severus, he is typically found in Manse Decados, consulting with his father on matters of state. Grigori is rarely found apart from his escort, Sasha Decados — a distant cousin whose role as escort is equally courtesan and bodyguard.

Roleplaying

Decados Characters

Decados Character Concepts

When creating or playing a Decados noble, consider the following questions:

What are your views on House Decados? Is it truly destined for greatness, or is it just a bunch of degenerates? Not every Decados is necessarily proud of his heritage.

What is your appearance like? Could you fit in at a Hawkwood ball, or would you stand out even amongst Decados? How do you wear your uniform? Do you have any unusual physical characteristics?

What is your reputation? Does Prince Hyram trust you explicitly? Or has the Jakovian Agency been going through your garbage? (Have a good reason for either extreme, of course.) Do other Decados respect/fear/admire you, or do they just see you as a stepping stone? How do non-Decados view you — a prince among thieves or a fox in the chicken coop?

Stereotypes

Here are some additional stereotypes:

- Selchakah distributor: As far as you're concerned, you have a legitimate business. Now the Church is breathing down your neck. As if business were easy anyway, what

with smuggling the drug to Byzantium Secundus, dealing with rivals, etc....

- Jakovian Agent: Yours is the mission of gathering information from across the Known Worlds, sometimes through means entirely unscrupulous. From lost civilizations to a Hawkwood's bedroom secrets — all are yours for the taking.

- Visionary: Your selchakah-induced visions have slowly become frightening, and now you see things that no one else can see. What is the connection between these visions and the fading suns?

- Decadent Diplomat: You have been charged with maintaining the peace with other houses. Unfortunately,

your own prurient interests have gotten you in trouble too many times.

- Political Exile: Your philosophical ideas are considered dangerous, and you've been exiled from your own homelands. (Considering the options, you're lucky.)

Gamemastering Decados

Gamemasters who run **Fading Suns** games with a strong Decados component can consider the following as potential plot hooks or storylines:

Grange Station: Characters living or working aboard the ancient Grange Station can encounter a number of situations, from discovering ancient technologies in the space station's bowels to unlocking the secret of the mysterious jumpgate (or being there when it mysteriously activates...), to thwarting (or aiding) schemes between the various parties present.

Malignatius Beckons: The characters travel to Malignatius to find a recluse whom they believe possesses vital knowledge which they need. Their transport is damaged, however, and before they can find the recluse they have to survive the cold and forbidding surface.

The Jakovian Contract: The characters have somehow gotten involved with the Jakovian Agency, and discover a secret conspiracy within the Agency that threatens to usurp House Decados and assassinate the Emperor.

In general, remember when running games with Decados elements that nothing should be straightforward, and the Decados pot is boiling over with conspiracies and suspicion.

Traits

Physical Affliction

Addiction (2-4 pts): The character is addicted to some substance, and this addiction makes his life difficult at times.

2 = Basic addiction. Substance is cheap and easily gotten. The character must have at least one dose per week before symptoms of withdrawal begin.

+1 = Stronger addiction: Substance must be had twice weekly before withdrawal symptoms begin.

+1 = Substance is difficult to find (rare or illegal).

Addiction to selchakah is a 3 pt addiction for Decados nobles (strong addiction), and 4 pts for non-Decados (for whom it is illegal) or Decados living and operating outside Decados territories.

Symptoms of withdrawal vary based upon the drug and the withdrawal period. Gamemasters may require Calm rolls, or assign goal penalties as the symptoms get worse — whatever increases the dramatic tension of a scene is appropriate.

For Honor and Glory: The Hazat

by Andrew Greenberg

Don Raphael Miguel Rolas de Selonia barely parried the steel blade thrust at his heart, for the blood streaming down his forehead made it almost impossible for him to see the sword's owner. His cousin, Baron Vaustus Ricardo Seste, danced back out of range of his riposte and began circling him once more. Don Raphael cursed the treacherous blackguard whose slug thrower had torn a wound across his forehead. That injury was now the difference in this duel, and Raphael's cousin would take full advantage of it.

That would be Baron Vaustus's way. Raphael now knew for certain that Vaustus had slain the former baron, Raphael's father, in order to claim the fief for himself. Raphael may never have discovered the truth had it not been for the mysterious package which arrived via space courier only a month ago. It contained a black cape, a mask and the sword he now wielded. It also contained a letter, begging Raphael to regain his family's honor.

Now Baron Vaustus dove in, his rapier seeking Raphael's throat. As Raphael moved to parry it, the blade flicked away, and Raphael twisted at the last moment to avoid being impaled in the groin. Baron Vaustus' feint had almost succeeded, and evading the blow left Raphael gasping for breath. His cousin's thin smile grew wider, and Raphael found himself backed up against the balcony railing.

Baron Vaustus had violently opposed Raphael's father in the old man's attempts to find common ground with the Emperor. Their arguments had grown more heated this year, with Vaustus calling for the Hazat to back his claims to Hawkwood land on Obun. After Raphael's father blocked these demands, he grew rapidly sick, and died several months later. The package arrived for Raphael shortly thereafter, somehow finding him on Grail where he and other Questing Knights were staying. He returned to Aragon, and found that Vaustus had lain claim to his father's barony.

Now, as Baron Vaustus prepared to renew his attack, Raphael desperately glanced around, seeking any way out. Baron Vaustus saw his distraction, and as he plunged forward, Raphael leapt for the balcony's curtains. He thrust his sword through the fabric as he felt a piercing pain in his side. Ignoring the new wound, he held on to the hilt of his blade as it cut through the curtain and carried him down three floors to the grand hall below. He heard his cousin laughing as he ran out into the night.

The Hazat

Some observers speak of the Hazat as beset from all sides. Certainly members of the house see themselves that way. The Caliphate encroaches on its rightful ownership of Kurga and threatens Vera Cruz. While its territory borders on three of the richest and most powerful worlds in human space — Holy Terra, Byzantium Secundus and Leagueheim — this both limits the house's expansion and creates a constant drain of money and resources going to those other worlds. The Hazat hoped that by making one of their own Emperor, they would be able to add Byzantium Secundus and Tethys to their sphere of influence, but found themselves left out in the cold when their Decados allies made peace with Emperor Alexius. Now the Hazat have to worry that the Emperor, Patriarch and Leaguemeister are all eyeing their territory.

So now the family is regrouping, taking stock of its assets and trying to prepare for the future. House leaders meet regularly to decide on a path, but as with any Hazat event, tempers fly and passions flare over the slightest disagreement. Should they push for a crusade against the heathen Kurgan? Actively seek to limit the Emperor's growing strength? Expand the house's influence on other worlds? Spend all their resources on strengthening their current holdings? The arguments continue long into the night, and more than a few Hazat are becoming frustrated by the proceedings.

While ancient ties bind all the house's disparate branches, these links are starting to fray. Hazat leaders on Sutek have begun voicing greater displeasure with the leadership on Aragon. Those on Vera Cruz have begun agitating for firmer action against the Caliphate. Finally,

and perhaps most worrisome, young Hazat have begun going elsewhere to make their name. Of course, this is nothing new for the house. The Hazat, perhaps more than any other noble house, seems to thrive on feelings of inferiority and persecution. Guild psychologists say these combine to drive individual Hazat to greater and greater feats of glory. A brief look at the house's history (which all Hazat learn while still very young) is all it takes to see these feelings in action.

History of the Hazat

House Chauki was one of the earliest families to rise from the collapse of the First Republic. Originally it was a federation of workers shipped to Aragon and other worlds from South America by TDA, a giant agribusiness conglomerate. It began as a social organization for several families, and slowly grew as those families became the most successful on what are now Aragon and Vera Cruz. While a number of members of this federation were successful TDA executives and security agents, the majority either worked on TDA farms or owned their own. All became less and less content with their lot, and began to wish for greater control over the massive farms they saw TDA running — and running dangerously wrong. In TDA's rush for profits, it had destroyed Aragon's great forests, driven its amazing zoological diversity to the brink of extinction, and set many of its workers in the equivalent of shanty towns, completely dependent on the company for all necessities.

When the Sathra revolts began, the Chauki saw their chance to correct these problems. Combining their resources, the Chauki federation's leaders bribed and cajoled Aragon's security forces into working for them. Since the security forces had little interest in joining the bloody battles going on in the Byzantium Secundus and Sutek systems, they agreed, in exchange for positions of power in the federation. When the Sathraist revolt ended, the Chaukis were in a position to demand changes from TDA. The corporation, flush with victory, refused to consider even the most minor of reforms.

In the ensuing battles, the Chauki found it necessary to legitimize their claim to power. Taking their hint from the growing noble houses, its leaders traced their Earthly ancestry. In 2553, Federation president Cesar de la Santo proudly announced his descent from Aztec King Montezuma and established the Chauki noble house. At his side was Emanuel Primitivo Hazat, formerly of the TDA security forces and now general of the Chauki army.

Claims to Nobility

At first the Chauki military was composed primarily of citizen volunteers. As time passed, and more people surrendered their freedoms in exchange for the security a noble lord could offer, this changed. The standing army became an elite force, supported in war time by levies from the population. The average peasant had to join the local militia but got little combat training. For almost a millennium this arrangement remained intact, with the Chaukis handling the political end of things and Hazat's descendants running the military.

As time went by, however, signs of friction became evident. The Hazat pushed for greater expansion, while the Chauki used far more of their wealth to develop the planets under their control. This friction reached a head near the end of the Second Republic, when one of Hazat's descendants, General Emanuel Huevo Iman (now Saint Emanuel), announced that House Chauki had conspired to hide the fact that Hazat was a descendant of King Alfonso XIII of Spain.

With the support of two other noble houses, Saint Emanuel moved quickly to overthrow House Chauki. The purge was total. Within a generation, the Hazat military and its allies had killed hundreds of Chauki, blaming them for crimes ranging from embezzlement to alien fraternization to genocide. Chauki sympathizers might cry out that Saint Emanuel was merely acting as a pawn for anti-Republic forces (House Chauki was one of the most powerful to support the Second Republic), but his success was undeniable. After the purge, which the Second Republic found itself unable to stop, Emanuel became one of the most prominent critics of the "Godless" Second Republic. Aragon became a center for anti-Republic forces — especially those running operations on Byzantium Secundus.

Such a threat this close to the capital of the Second Republic should have caused greater concern, but immediately after the last Chauki strolled out an airlock without putting on his space suit, catastrophes began to wrack the Second Republic. While welfare riots and then religious hysteria struck Byzantium Secundus, the Hazat consolidated their power. When aliens and rogue worlders attacked the planet, the Hazat helped lead the charge that drove off the attackers, destroyed the Second Republic and established the Hazat as one of the leading houses.

The Hazat wanted to claim immediate possession of Byzantium Secundus, but the other nine leading noble houses opposed that. Instead, the Hazat began spreading to other planets where the Chauki had held influence. When minor houses on Vera Cruz tried to stop them, the Hazat unleashed the full strength of their military. For the first time the houses saw the true strength of the Hazat in action. Superbly trained and equipped nobles led their forces into battle. They whipped their soldiers up into a frenzy before unleashing them upon their targets. In no time at all the minor houses found themselves driven almost to the point of extinction.

Finally House Alecto, which also had substantial investments on the planet, stepped in to stop the destruction. Clashes between the two houses became common, but before it could escalate into all-out war, the Patriarch intervened. In one of the first instances of the Church demonstrating control over the nobility, he forced the two houses to divide up the planet between them. House Alecto welcomed the interference, but the Hazat seethed under the new restrictions.

Each time the Hazat seemed to be gaining more territory and influence, something similar would happen. Efforts to grab Leagueheim and Madoc were blocked by the League, though the Hazat managed to maintain some influence there. Efforts to bypass Holy Terra and seize Artemis and Pentateuch were blocked by the Church. Several other worlds falling under Hazat sway, like Heaven's Ridge and Dashwood, suddenly found themselves cut off, their jump routes to the Known Worlds sundered and the Hazat on those worlds lost. Then came the Barbarian Invasions.

The Barbarian Invasions

The main attacks came from what is now the Vuldrok border, but no few assaults came from the growing Kurga Caliphate. Both House Alecto and the Hazat suffered from these. At first the Hazat reveled in the opportunity to expand via battle, but as the battles continued, they found themselves on the defensive. The pure magnitude of the invasion began to tax the resources of all the Known Worlds. As more and more worlds lost contact with the rest of humanity, key products disappeared. The Hazat had never created a strong manufacturing base, and soon the house could barely construct the most basic of weapons. As the war dragged on, mounting any sort of offensive became next to impossible.

Despite this, when Vladimir Alecto approached Princess Juandilla Eleonora Justus de Aragon about uniting forces against the barbarians, the Hazat refused — at first. Then, as they felt greater and greater pressure applied from all sides, they reluctantly agreed. Hazat forces entered battle under the leadership of Alecto and Windsor nobles, and slowly the barbarian tide was stopped. The Hazat took control of much of Kurga and began re-equipping their forces at once.

Vladimir's dreams of an empire at peace turned to ash the moment he put the crown on his head. Hazat forces entered battle as soon as word of the assassination reached their ships over Byzantium Secundus. They opened fire on the Alecto fleet, destroying Vladimir's flagship in the process. Within a week, Hazat troops had taken the field against House Alecto, sending the unprepared, leaderless forces scurrying.

No other house could come to the Alecto's aid, and it was only a matter of years before the house's last fief lay in ruins. In the confusing times after Vladimir's death, there was no one to keep the Hazat and the Alecto's other enemies from destroying the house which had once claimed an empire. While no one knows exactly who killed the last Alecto, the Hazat are at least as responsible for the destruction as anyone else.

War Within

The end of House Alecto should have provided the Hazat with a golden opportunity to extend their power, but they, like many of the other houses, squandered their chance. Instead of sharing power equally within the family, different branches sought to promote their own agendas. At first this happened quietly, with the branches slowly calling their own troops home, leaving the frontiers guarded only by those who had a direct stake in their security. Then the action began to heat up.

The Castenda branch, led by Duke Afonzo Craftia Castenda de Sutek, demanded fiefs on Vera Cruz since the Bursandra branch had managed to seize much of Kurga. Princess Juandilla tried to mediate the dispute but found herself dragged into it as other house branches took sides. Hostilities became common as duels between individual nobles turned into full-fledged brawls and then military skirmishes. Daring commando raids by one branch against another began to occur, and other houses began watching the situation, looking to take advantage of the strife.

The most extreme change happened on Aragon itself, where the branch now known as the Eduardos broke off from the Justus branch. With the tacit approval of the other members of the family, the Eduardos took control of the famous Aragon military academy. An Eduardo became archbishop of Aragon, and soon its officers commanded most of the Hazat troops on the planet. The Justus branch maintained its immense land holdings but took a back seat in family politics.

For the next several hundred years bickering continually stymied efforts to expand the house's power and almost led to the house's break up on several different occasions. The years before the Emperor Wars saw the Hazat at their most fragmented, with different factions gearing up for war. It took a marriage between Princess Louevi Semonista Eduardo de Callondra and Duke Warren Hamon Esuigi Justus de Goldenrod to keep Aragon from collapsing into perpetual violence. They united the planet and from their union came Prince Juan Jacobi Nelson Eduardo de Aragon, who proceeded to use both force and diplomacy to bring Vera Cruz and Sutek into line.

The Emperor Wars and Beyond

Prince Juan saw the Emperor Wars as a critical opportunity for his house. When Prince Darius Hawkwood made his move, Prince Juan used it as leverage against the other family branches. He convinced them that without a strong alliance, their planets would be the first to fall to the Hawkwood. This convincing also required an assault on Sutek, but the Castendas quickly capitulated.

The Hazat had long coveted Byzantium Secundus, and it became one of Prince Juan's earliest targets. When Baron Miguel Amahedra Rolas was assassinated there, Prince Juan personally led the Hazat forces in their quest for vengeance. They seized large chunks of the planet but, before they could press their claim, al-Malik, Hawkwood, Li Halan and Church fleets came through the jumpgate. The Hazat promised to leave Byzantium Secundus inviolate for the rest of the wars, sacked what parts of the planet had come under their control and took off with enough wealth to fund their war machine for several years.

This promise fell by the wayside when Alexius finally declared himself Emperor. Immediately the Hazat and Decados launched attacks on the planet. They failed to coordinate their offenses, however, and Alexius had little trouble defeating first one, repairing his forces, and then defeating the other. After a clandestine meeting between Duchess Salandra Decados and Duke Jose Alfonso Louis Eduardo de Aragon, the two houses finally managed to coordinate their assaults.

The Hazat came through the jumpgate first, bringing a mighty fleet from Aragon to tear at Alexius's first line of defense. Their attack reached Byzantium Secundus' moon before their energy was spent. Fast behind them came the Decados, whose fleet had rendezvoused at Pyre, and the epic Siege of Jericho was joined. At first it looked as though Alexius's dreams of empire would die on that airless moon. A critical base, from here the Decados and Hazat would be able to rain down death on the planet below. With no atmosphere to contend with, their attacks would require almost no energy, while the Hawkwoods would use up most of their energy reserves just trying to get off planet.

The Decados's massive assault on the planet was accompanied by a massive bombardment from orbit. Alexius himself led a desperate counterattack to break the siege in space, but the combined Hazat-Decados fleet could not be budged. No one knows whether what happened next was planned or accidental, but as the bulk of the Decados army stormed across the moon, its defense shields failed — or were turned off. A rain of fire poured out of the sky and hit the moon's fragile fusion generators. Explosion after explosion erupted, and soon everyone on the satellite, Hawkwood, Decados, Hazat and innocents alike, had died.

With their armies wrecked, the Hazat and Decados had no choice but to retreat. Alexius took advantage of the reprieve to rebuild his forces, and reinforcements hired from the Muster and borrowed from the al-Malik began to arrive. At this point Prince Juan saw no other choice but to recognize Alexius' rule. The fact that the Kurga Caliphate was beginning to attack Vera Cruz played no little role in this decision.

Now the Hazat find themselves as they have long believed themselves to be. They present a facade of unity while contesting mightily with each other. They see enemies on all sides, and believe that only the most heroic of acts will see them through. Of course, even if they lose they will have fought the good fight.

Hazat Culture and Ways

Some unperceptive observers believe that the Hazat have the most cohesive of all the noble houses. After all, in the field the Hazat have a very rigid chain of command which no member of the family would dare violate. This hierarchy only applies to the field, however. In the field, a knight may end up commanding a baron, and the baron will submit willingly. Later, at the victory party, that same knight had better show real deference to the baron, or there will be trouble.

Still, the Hazat rules of behavior are constantly in flux. The only hard-and-fast rule is that orders given either during a battle or in preparation for one are inviolate. Once out of combat, Hazat are left to their own devices in deciding how to act. Basic rules of etiquette should be followed, of course, but each Hazat must steer his own course. Etiquette usually comes in second to the drive for glory.

The Path to Glory

There are only two recognized ways for a Hazat to gain a greater title — and more holdings. The first (and most common) way is to inherit a title. They pass to the deceased's first natural born child (of either gender). If a noble dies without having sired or given birth, then the title passes to any adopted children. If there are no adopted

Hazat Names

Some wags joke that you can tell how important a Hazat is by how many names he has. While most people in the Known Worlds have a proper name and a surname, and a fair number have a middle name, people on Hazat planets tend toward more elaborate constructions. Even peasants tend to take the name of their grandfather, grandmother, uncle, great aunt and some local hero.

A Hazat will be more than happy to tell anyone who asks (and some who don't) the history behind his extensive name. Each name has some meaning, and the Hazat are almost always proud of whoever bore that name before. After all, whoever had it before was also named after someone noteworthy, and so on and so forth down the line.

Hazat also tend to take appellations based on events or places important to them. Someone of importance on the planet Sutek, like the Duke, may take the appellation "de Sutek" following his name. A Hazat whose fief includes a large city might add that to her name, as in "de Toledo." Others might name themselves after their first battle, as is the case with Juan Elabaro Hustin de Jericho (see below).

children, then it goes to her oldest living sibling. If there is no such sibling, then it goes to the oldest nephew or niece. If there are no nephews or nieces, then it goes through the lists of cousins. This sometimes ends up with a person having multiple titles, though the Hazat rarely attach more than one to their names.

The second way is to earn a title. All Hazat are knighted upon reaching the age of 12, though some delay this distinction until they have proven themselves through some rite of passage. Those who are not the first born know that the only way to advance is gain the admiration of some higher-ranking Hazat, who can elevate her to a title just below his own. Some do this by serving their older siblings, who in turn promote them for doing their duty to the family. Thus Baroness Jessica Francine Assestra Bursandra might make her brother a baronet after that brother has helped her run the family estate for a number of years. These promotions might come with holdings, though these holdings may go back to those who made the promotion upon the death of the newly appointed.

A better way to earn a title is through acts of personal glory. The Emperor Wars were a great time for lower-born Hazat to rise through the ranks. Battlefield promotions were not uncommon, and even Prince Juan gave up a number of his holdings to nobles who distinguished themselves in battle. The fact that many died during the wars, and their lands either went to their descendants or their feudal overlords, took a back seat to this unparal-

leled opportunity. Now that the wars are over, young nobles have begun looking to other places for a chance to earn greater title. The Kurga Caliphate, the Symbiots and even the Questing Knights have become beacons for these knights, offering the chance for them to prove themselves and gain stature within the house.

Rites of Passage

While the idea of rites of passage has gone in and out of style among the Hazat, it has never fully lost the fascination it holds for younger nobles. This desire to prove themselves drives them to greater and greater feats, though at least a few would call these feats of idiocy. Young Hazat, many still children, will take a small entourage into some place of danger to prove that they should be treated as adults.

These expeditions may be as simple as a safari to some isolated part of Vera Cruz, tracking a bandit into the slums of Aragon, or defeating a Hawkwood in a race from one planet to the next. More ambitious Hazat will travel to Kurga to raid the barbarians. The most ambitious will go all the way to Stigmata to fight the Symbiots. Rumor has it that the jump route to Kurga was rediscovered by a young Hazat on his rite of passage, but that would have happened many centuries ago.

While some Hazat parents send extremely competent guardians to keep an eye on their impetuous children, others send their children off to sink or swim on their own. Not a few Hazat have suffered grievous defeats by overestimating what they are capable of, but most return the better for their experience. They often gain staunch allies, important skills and a critical awareness of what the universe is like outside the safety of their family mansion.

Fashion

Caught between Byzantium Secundus and Leagueheim, the Hazat find themselves pressured to meet the styles being set on both those planets. As a result, the Hazat often find themselves the most colorfully accoutered of any nobles (except the al-Malik). Their style is often a mishmash, featuring the tight leggings popular on Byzantium Secundus and the loose ruffled shirts of Leagueheim. This can make them the butt of other nobles' jokes, but the Hazat can often carry off these combinations since the bodies which wear them are usually fit and attractive.

Indeed, if there is any constant to Hazat fashion, it is that they like to show off their bodies. All three of the main Hazat planets are slightly warmer than Holy Terra, and the Hazat are used to dressing for the weather. It is not uncommon for male and female nobles to go topless when they are relaxing (especially on Sutek), and skirts have become popular with men on Vera Cruz. Hazat on Aragon and Sutek tend to wear a great deal of jewelry, with the Castenda branch on Sutek sporting a wide variety of body piercings. No other branch likes body piercings. They are far too much of a liability in combat.

Honor vs. Glory

One of the oldest schisms in the house also creates conflict within many individual nobles. This is the desire for personal glory as weighed against the need for honor. Leading Hazat, including most barons and all dukes, hammer home the role of honor above all else. Glory without honor is meaningless, they say, and those who act dishonorably cast scorn on the entire house.

Younger Hazat, on the other hand, point out that the nobles who most often promote this view have already taken their place at the top of the house. For nobles without an inherited title to reach the same level, they will have to engage in innumerable feats of daring. Honor must sometimes be sacrificed when the opportunity for self-advancement appears.

The house holds the most esteem for those nobles who successfully achieve both of these goals. Princess Louevi, Prince Juan's deceased mother, is often held up as the epitome of these virtues. She ended all contact with her true love in order to reunite Aragon through marriage and then led the Hazat forces which helped bring Vera Cruz and Sutek into line, all the while keeping the pressure on the Hawkwoods and the Li Halan. Prince Juan has dedicated all his victories to his mother's memory, and more than a few knights have pledged themselves to carrying on her example. The most prominent of these is Baroness Lucinda Dulcinea, now the commander of the Stigmata Garrison.

Dueling

Dueling has become a common way for Hazat to maintain these competing ideals. Fencing is one of earliest skills a Hazat child learns, often being taught by other children. Hazat fencing instruction lacks the subtlety of that given to the Hawkwoods and the Decados, making up what it lacks in refinement with sheer force. While other houses prefer rapiers and epees, Hazat go for the dueling saber. When fighting members of other houses a Hazat might stoop to using a lighter blade, but when fighting another Hazat, the shields are turned off and the heavy sabers picked up.

Swords are not the only dueling weapons the Hazat utilize. The participants can bring whatever weapons they agree upon, and often the only stipulations are "No guns and no shields." Fists, daggers, battle axes, halberds and wireblades have all found their place in Hazat duels. Even guns are occasionally used, but only when the wrong being contested is especially grievous.

Most Hazat duels are a time of great revelry, with all nearby Hazat nobles showing up to egg on the contestants. Local dignitaries from other houses (and sometimes the League) are invited, and serfs from all over sneak into safe places to watch the fight. The two duelists will recite their family pedigree and then dramatically argue the point which has put them in conflict. When one or the other tires of arguing, the weapons come out and the bets are placed.

Most duels last until one or the other participants surrenders. For minor points of honor, or when they are just fighting to see who is better, this usually ends with first blood. Unfortunately, with the hot-blooded Hazat, fights often last until one duelist can no longer continue. When the insult has been too great, death is a probable outcome.

The Domino and Rapier

A domino is a black cape and mask often worn to balls or masquerade parties. For the Hazat, however, it has a more important meaning, linked to a specific cape. The identity of the first Hazat to wear the Domino to right some wrong has been lost in the mists of time, but all members of the family know the legends. The Domino and rapier will arrive from parts unknown for a Hazat who has been chosen to regain personal or family honor. It is then her responsibility to seek out whoever it was that committed this wrong and wreak vengeance.

Some of the more famous situations involving the Domino have included those whose lands were wrongfully taken or whose reputations had been falsely impugned. The Domino itself is known to be armored like synthsilk, and all who have used the rapier swear that it seems to drive them to regain their honor, almost fighting on its own when the need arises.

Wearing the Domino is a great responsibility, but not all who have done so have succeeded. More than a few have died in the process. What has never happened, however, is for a Hazat wearing the Domino to act dishonorably. No one knows whether this is due to the Domino itself or the inherent goodness of those chosen to wear it. In addition, no one knows, or admits to knowing, who sends out the Domino. Some believe that the previous wearer is responsible for sending it on, while others believe that it goes back to a cabal of Hazat leaders. Even most of the wearers have never been positively identified.

The Domino itself is made of an unidentifiable black material similar to synthsilk. It covers the wearer's face and back, though many users have managed to use the cloak to protect all parts of their bodies. Opponents trying to avoid hitting the Domino need to make an aimed attack with a -4 modifier.

The Rapier

The rapier seems to be a standard blade, but it is the heart of the Domino's power. Crafted centuries ago on a lost world and made from a metal now forgotten, it was empowered by one of the first Hazat masters of the psychic Soma path. It gives its wielder a +10 (!) to incite Passion for righting the wrong which has been done. This has helped wearers of the Domino (referred to as the Domino while on their righteous quest) cut their way through hordes of enemies, climb sheer mountain faces, and survive the most extreme torments imaginable. It also reduces

wound penalties by 2, so a wound that took the character to -2 would have no noticeable impact, while one that took him to -10 would only be at -8. This does not give the character extra Vitality, however; once his own Vitality has been used up, he's still a goner.

Hazat Holdings

When two Hazat compare their worth, money and pedigree certainly play a role. These are not the most critical areas for comparison, however. For most Hazat, the lands his family has seized over time, the lands he himself has seized, and those he has successfully defended have far more value. Any guild swine can accumulate firebirds. Even the weakest al-Malik can claim descent from some great leader. A true noble knows that value comes from the earth, and one's own value is proved by how well he has maintained and extended those holdings.

The average Hazat estate has been in the family for generations. It consists primarily of farm land, though mining and industry certainly have their place. Most control at least one town, though this can vary from the muddiest villages to the beautiful resort cities of Vera Cruz. Peasants have limited freedom of mobility, though moving from one fief to another is actively discouraged. If people keep moving, how are nobles going to be able to get their legions together at a moment's notice?

Middle-aged nobles, those whose days of active combat are just ending, take charge of the fiefs' day-to-day operations. Older Hazat become more like teachers and mentors, giving advice and direction but staying out of the nitty gritty. Other important members of the household staff include the seneschal, who carries out the fief holder's orders, the commander of the legions, and the prefect, who is in charge of teaching Hazat children as well as some specially chosen freemen youth. Most Hazat households include a large gymnasium, stables and some barracks as well as the normal manorial buildings.

Aragon

The crown jewel of the Hazat is Aragon, home of shining spires, ancient castles, famous diamond mines, glorious battles and some of the most legendary warriors ever to walk the Known Worlds. What is less well known are the wretched slums of unemployed legionnaires, the violent desert nomads, and the constant feud between the Eduardo and Justus branches.

The center of Hazat power is the glorious palace and war college on the west coast of Quechua, the planet's largest continent. The center of Quechua is desert and the east coast has some of the planet's richest farm land, owned by the Justus branch of the family. The Eduardo branch controls the west coast, including the planet's main industrial holdings. This industrial section is still retooling from the massive military buildup of the Emperor Wars, when almost the entirety of the planet's resources were turned over to the war effort.

Most of the serfs who were called away from their jobs to serve in the armed forces have returned to their earlier callings. Most work the land, but more than a few have ended up in the growing slums around Aragon's factories. Crime has leapt incredibly in the past three years, turning these tenements into hot beds of violence and dissent. The Hazat have not made any effort to bring them under control — Aragon's dangerous slums have always been a breeding ground for excellent soldiers, and the Hazat believe current conditions are just part of that process.

Castle Furias

This is the main palace of the Hazat. It once belonged to the Justus branch, but when the Eduardos broke away, they took the palace as one of their holdings. This breathtakingly beautiful complex is as defensible as it is gorgeous. Its battlements are an intrinsic part of its architecture, and its armor glistens like crystal.

For generations the Justus branch spent vast sums making the building even more sumptuous, and the Eduardos have continued this process. During the Emperor Wars several Hazat knights found St. Bernado's Globe of Infinite Wonderment in a Diaspora-era ruin on Vera Cruz. The Eduardos smuggled it off planet and brought it to Castle Furias, where it now sits in the center of the main chapel. No one can deny that the castle has appeared more resplendent since its additions, and serfs have begun to visit the globe as a pilgrimage. Rumor has it that those who view the stone become both more aware of their deepest desires (+8 Introvert while in its presence) and more committed to those desires (+4 Passion while in its presence).

Vera Cruz

Vera Cruz lacks many of the industrial problems which afflict Aragon, but that is because it also lacks that planet's industry. The only important industry on the planet is agriculture, though there is a little bit of mining on the planet's only sizable continent. The Bursandra branch of the family owns most of the planet's land, and they have built a gorgeous palace on Dorado, a beautiful island just off the coast of the main continent.

Vera Cruz suffered almost no damage during the Emperor Wars but is now threatened by the Kurga Caliphate. The Hazat know that the Kurgans desperately want to seize Vera Cruz. Indeed, those prisoners the Hazat have captured have told them that they feel it is their holy duty to "liberate" the planet. A number of Eskatonic and Avestite priests have established a monastery on the planet's arctic continent. There they research Kurgan claims regarding the planet, but nothing of note has been reported.

The Hazat like to promote Vera Cruz as their least military-oriented planet, but this is changing as the Kurgan conflict becomes more active. Many landless knights have flocked here trying to earn a piece of the lost world, and Vera Cruz's nobles have begun to call in troops from their underlings on other planets. On top of this, a number of Hazat, especially those of the Rolas and Dulcinea branches, are secret practitioners of the Soma psychic path. They have a hidden training facility on Vera Cruz, well away from prying eyes.

Sutek

Originally known as Sathra's Boon, Sutek has had the longest human habitation of any world other than Holy Terra. The Sathra movement had its greatest strength here, and this is where the earliest battles against its adherents took place. The First Republic claimed to have completely destroyed all traces of the movement, and took extra care to annihilate its adherents here, but rumors persisted that the heresy had survived.

House Chauki claimed this planet during the Diaspora, swearing to protect humanity from any renewal of the Sathra threat. By the time of the Second Republic the house had lost much of its hold on the world. It became an industrial center during that period and benefited greatly from its proximity to Urth and Byzantium Secundus. The collapse of the Second Republic devastated Sutek. The Hazat renewed the old Chauki claim to the planet, and the Castenda branch moved in. The Church adamantly objected but was in too much disarray to stop this move.

Over the years the Castendas solidified their hold on the planet, though many claim Sutek has solidified its hold over them. Indeed, there have been many times when the Castendas appeared ready to break off from the Hazat and form their own house. Only the threat of a Church move on the planet has kept them from doing so. The Church has always had a strong distrust of anything associated with what was once Sathra's Boon, and many Castendas fear that if they did break off from the house's protection, nothing would stop the Patriarch from moving in.

The Dervishes

Deep in the rain forests of Vera Cruz, far to the south of the family's main holdings, is the St. Sondra monastery, a hermitage with no ties to the Church. It is here that Hazat followers of the Soma path of psychic power gather to practice their techniques. Most members of the Hazat are unaware of this facility, though leading members of most of the family's branches have given it their tacit approval. Officially founded in 4970 by Baroness Camilia Marlane Rolas, a veteran of the Kurgan wars, it took advantage of the number of psychic Hazat who had appeared on Vera Cruz. The existence of psychic warriors had long been hidden by the house, but the Emperor Wars gave them reason to try to organize this asset.

The Hazat secretly fielded their first psychic unit, composed mostly of minor nobles, in 4979. There were never many of these small units, but their effectiveness was undeniable. Gifted primarily in Soma but also talented in other paths as well, they could wreak havoc on unsuspecting opponents. Their existence is one of the reasons the Hazat make such fearsome enemies.

By the end of the Emperor Wars the existence of these units was no longer a secret to the other noble houses, some of which organized their own psychic soldiers into legions. These legionnaires came to be called "dervishes", though all the houses officially disbanded their groups when they recognized Alexius. These psychic troops remained a secret from the peasantry all along, though rumors could never be quashed.

Kurga

The jump route from Vera Cruz to this jungle world has closed and reopened more than any other. House Chauki controlled this planet prior to the Hazat uprising, and before the Hazat could consolidate their hold, the Kurgans closed the jumpgate. When it reopened centuries later, the Hazat branch on the planet had changed dramatically, and controlled very little of it. The Justus branch sent a number of legions over to reassert control, and the jump route closed again. It reopened again shortly after the birth of Vladimir, and the Hazat found that something called the Kurga Caliphate had risen to power.

This began the war between the two groups. During this 500-year feud the jumproute has opened and closed on numerous occasions — usually whenever the Kurgans are losing. The last reopening was almost 100 years ago, and Hazat scientists believe that the Kurgans somehow caused this change, and the house believes that only a concerted effort to retake the planet can keep it from happening again.

Hazat holdings on the planet are centered around the uranium-rich mountains of the south, where they have made an alliance with House Shelit, a minor house which has long been at odds with the Caliphate. The Hazat have been trying to push into the fertile lowlands to the north of their holdings, and the farms here have been the scene of some violent clashes. Still, the Hazat are only now beginning to bring the full weight of their military to bear, and most off-planet Hazat feel a full offensive is imminent.

Other Planets

The Hazat have numerous investments on other planets, though control of these worlds is beyond their current ability. While the house is best known for military conquest, its members have no fear of using their wealth to establish a foothold on a planet. Then the troops can be called in to protect Hazat lives and property.

Byzantium Secundus

The Hazat have made no secret of their desire for this world. They wanted it in 4000, when they joined the Ten in retaking the planet. They tried to take it during the Emperor Wars and sacked much of it when other noble houses united to drive them off. They were careful not to touch those parts of it which their own nobles owned, however.

Much of this Hazat control is secret. They own property and industries through fronts and other noble houses. Since the Emperor Wars, the Justus and Eduardo branches have been funneling funds through several minor houses. House Cameton, which officially rules Byzantium Secundus, used to be friendly with the Hazat — until the Hazat tore up much of their industry. Now the Hazat make up what must be the most unpopular house on the planet, as well as one of the most powerful.

Holy Terra

As Church leaders expected, the Hazat began eyeing Earth after they seized Sutek. Hazat nobles established villas on the planet and began extending their hold. This unintentionally helped solidify the Church, as a synod of religious leaders gathered to claim Holy Terra as the physical and spiritual birthplace of all humanity. They managed to bring the entire planet under their sway before the Hazat could mobilize, and the Patriarch became the de facto lord of Holy Terra.

Since then the Church has been buying up more and more of the planet, so that even those few minor houses on the planet are in thrall to the Patriarch. The Hazat knows that an attack on the planet would be the greatest folly the house could accomplish, so they move slowly, hoping to gain chunks of the planet if not the whole thing. To that end they have made substantial investments in South America and Western Europe — two areas where the Church's control is occasionally challenged.

Pentateuch and Artemis

The Church has also kept the Hazat from adding these two worlds to their collection, but the Hazat investment on these worlds is still obvious. Members of the Castenda branch rule parts of Pentateuch while most of the branches have at least one fief on Artemis. On both worlds the Hazat must also contend with Hawkwood fiefs.

Despite its proximity to Delphi, Pentateuch may be the Hazat's best chance for adding to their dominion. Should charges of heresy against the Eskatonic Order ever be proved, the Hazat would move on this world in an instant. No faction has an overwhelming military presence on this world, and the Hazat may well be able to mobilize faster than anyone else. Of course, that may be part of the reason the Patriarch has not acted against the Eskatonics.

Obun

Among those calling for a crackdown on "alien influence" are those Hazat with land on Obun. The house has several baronies on this planet, all of them almost 1000 years old. On most worlds these baronies would have been combined into a duchy by now, but the Hazat on Obun have never pledged themselves to anyone but the house leader. Hazat on other worlds joke bitterly about how often the Obun branch comes demanding aid and how infrequently that same branch is willing to assist anyone else.

The only way the Hazat on Obun kept from being driven off during the Emperor Wars was by taking absolutely no action against House Hawkwood. Near the end of the war even their payments to their own house became infrequent, leading to innumerable threats back and forth. Now that the war is over and their position seems safe, they have again begun pressing their claims to more land on the planet. The only group who seems to want to block these claims more than House Hawkwood are the Ur-Obun themselves.

Tethys

Hazat involvement on this planet is a very recent affair, really only beginning after Vladimir's death and only getting serious after the Emperor Wars ended. Hazat moves on this planet, which involve buying lands not officially owned by the Emperor, have been supported and covertly funded by House Decados and the Reeves as a check against the Emperor's power. The Hazat presence on Tethys barely equals a barony, but it is seen as an important foothold should Alexius try to overreach himself.

The Kurga Caliphate

The Kurga Caliphate came into existence at least 500 years ago and is one of the barbarian groups that Vladimir united humanity against. While not as much of a threat to the Known Worlds then as the Hazat believe it to be

now, it created enough concern to convince Princess Juandilla to support the would-be emperor. The jumpgate to Kurga closed shortly after Vladimir's death, only to re-open a decade later. Each time the jumpgate shuts down the Caliphate seems to grow more powerful.

Despite the Hazat's long war against the Caliphate, they have discovered little about it. Kurgan soldiers rarely surrender, seeming to prefer death to captivity, and those who have been captured turn out to be poorly educated fanatics. Church leaders have pressured the Hazat to let them take control of Kurgan prisoners, and have stressed that all Kurgans encountered so far are heretics. The Hazat have used this ruling to pressure the Church to call for a crusade against the Caliphate, but no Patriarch has done so. The Church has been far too busy trying to establish its own dominion over the Known Worlds. Now that the Emperor has stymied this effort, however...

Most of the Kurgans encountered on Kurga have been short and swarthy, though this is by no means true of everyone in the Caliphate. Kurgans seem to sport the same scope of physical diversity as is found in the Empire, but most of those encountered have come from Kurga itself. Kurga is certainly only one world in the Caliphate, and captured Kurgans call it Hira, while the natives have a number of names for the planet.

The Kurgans religion seems similar in many ways to that of the Universal Church, but Church scholars have deemed it heretical and an unacceptable departure from the Prophet's teachings. That it has fired up the Kurgan's ferocity is undeniable; they fight with a ferocity matched only by the Church's own religious leaders. Some Hazat who have infiltrated behind Kurgan lines believe that the Kurgans have their own equivalent of a crusade in effect, with Vera Cruz as its main objective.

The Hazat Family

Like most royal houses, the Hazat has its own sub-groups, generally referred to as the family branches. These branches coordinate their efforts very effectively in the field, with all nobles knowing their role and carrying it out to the best of their abilities. Off the battlefield, however, things are quite the opposite. Each family branch seems to have its own goals, and individual members their own agendas. The competing ideals of honor and glory again rear their heads, and the conflict remains unresolved. Six of the most prominent branches are detailed below.

The Eduardo Branch

Currently the official leaders of the Hazat, the Eduardo branch broke off from the Justus (pronounced HOO-stus) branch in 4609, claiming Castle Furias on Aragon. Castle Furias and St. Bernado's Globe of Infinite Wonderment have long been the symbols of Hazat leadership, and the Eduardo's success in keeping the Justus branch from reclaiming these icons solidified their position. They have maintained their position at the top with a strong mix of diplomacy and military might which reached its peak during the Emperor Wars. The Eduardos, lead by Prince Juan and his cousin, Duke Jose (currently on Byzantium Secundus) kept the house operating at high levels of efficiency. Now that the war is over, however, other branches have begun to whisper that the Eduardos failed. Unless the Eduardos can find another cause to unite the Hazat, their days on top may be numbered.

The Justus Branch

The Justus claim to be the direct descendants of both Emanuel Primitivo Hazat and Saint Emanuel, two of the most venerated Hazat of ancient history. They have always been one of the house's leading branches, and their members claimed the prince (or princess) title from about 4100 until 4609, when the Eduardos broke off. The Justus branch is still recognized as the richest among the Hazat, and they control much of Aragon's arable land.

They seem to have taken their fall from the heights of power with good grace, mounting only a perfunctory challenge to the Eduardos. The fact that most of the other family branches supported the Eduardos surely had something to do with this, but the Justuses could have caused more trouble than they did. Some say the Justuses have just been biding their time, for should the Eduardos stumble now, the Justus branch is in the best position to displace them.

The Castenda

Some Eduardos have been known to jokingly argue whether the Castenda are still a part of the Hazat or if they

---

The Crusade

Shortly before the Emperor Wars began, the Hazat called for a crusade against the Kurga Caliphate. This crusade would have brought much of the Known Worlds' military might to bear, and would have thrown together the religious orders, house troops and even the League under either Hazat or Church leadership. This might have happened had the Emperor Wars not made it an impossibility. Now that the wars are over, a number of Hazat have again begun agitating for a crusade.

The al-Malik actively oppose this move, saying that it would draw off forces from the Symbiot War. The Hazat counter that the al-Malik are only afraid of having their people under Church leadership and secretly hint at ties between the al-Malik and Kurgans. The Emperor has not given any indication that he would support such a crusade, but a number of Hawkwood nobles have joined the Hazat in this call, for they want the crusade directed against the Vuldrok as well.

broke off to join their true masters — the Decados. The Castenda branch was close to the Decados before and during the Emperor Wars, though how close they are now is an unanswered question. After all, when the Hazat finally made peace with Alexius, the legions stationed on Sutek almost mutinied, demanding another chance to attack Byzantium Secundus — with or without Decados aid.

The Castenda are the most powerful nobles on Sutek, the first planet humanity colonized. Sutek has long been considered one of the oddest of the Known Worlds, and its inhabitants are unlike those found on any other planet. It has come under the close scrutiny of the Church on numerous occasions and, despite its close proximity to Holy Terra, is still considered a world at risk. The Church seems especially worried about heretical sects popping up in ruins from ancient human societies. The Castenda officially say that all the ancient ruins have been explored and that there is nothing left to find, but they still have their own agents looking into every nook and cranny of the planet.

The Bursandra

The Bursandra used to have a reputation as the Hazat's least militaristic branch, but that is beginning to change. Once their fiefs on Vera Cruz were considered some of the most secure, protected by Aragon and Sutek from attack by other houses. Then began the barbarian wars. Now that peace (of a sort) has descended on the Known Worlds, Vera Cruz is the Hazat's most threatened world, and it is here (and Kurga) that the Bursandra have most of their fiefs.

The Bursandra have used their long-standing influence in the Church to start pushing for a holy crusade against the Kurga Caliphate. The most warlike Bursandra have usually ended up in one of the orders of religious knights, and no few members of this branch have become bishops and even archbishops. They see their beautiful fiefs on Vera Cruz threatened and are willing to go to any extreme to protect them.

The Rolas

The Rolas branch is spread throughout Hazat territory but has still managed to earn a strong reputation as the house's most successful warriors. All Rolas, no matter what planet they grow up on, receive an intense education in all aspects of war. While almost all Hazat consider themselves superior combatants, the Rolas take this to an extreme. Nothing is as important to the Rolas as their military prowess.

While this means that the Rolas are rarely the richest or most respected Hazat on a planet, other Hazat consider their presence on a world as crucial. When in doubt, they can always turn to a Rolas to lead that charge against overwhelming odds or defend a position to the last breath.

The Dulcinea

The Dulcinea are another small branch, but one that has earned its distinction through honorable actions as

well as success in combat. While the Rolas branch trains in combat from birth, the Dulcineas have ethics and morals drilled into them. For them, maintaining the house's honor and then their own are the two leading requirements.

While the Dulcinea have some fiefs on all three of the main Hazat worlds, they are gaining strength with the Hazat expansions on other planets. They have land on Tethys, Artemis, Byzantium Secundus and Holy Terra, and seek to expand further into areas that do not traditionally belong to the Hazat.

The Estancia

The Estancia are freemen, not a branch of the family. Still, their role in Hazat society equals that of some of the minor branches. Almost all of the Estancia (or their ancestors) received grants of land in exchange for exceptional valor as members of the Hazat legions. They maintain a position of respect and power in most small communities, where they often serve as liaisons with the Hazat ruler or as judges, deciding local disputes.

Not all the Estancia get to pass their positions on to their children. The number of Estancia grew during the Emperor Wars, but many of these were temporary grants of freedom, and the lands that went with them will return to the gifting noble after the Estancia's death. Still, the number of Estancia is currently rather high, and they could easily turn into an exceptionally important part of Hazat life.

Prominent Hazat

Don Marcika Holuzio Rolas

Don Marcika wields a great deal of power for someone of his rank, most of which comes from his position as leader of the Hazat dervishes. While the legions of Hazat psychics have officially been disbanded, a number of dervishes have followed Marcika to Kurga, where he now battles the Caliphate.

His troops make up an elite legion, and are used for infiltration, sabotage and as reserves to be deployed when battles are critical. The Hazat have found that the Kurgans have their own form of dervishes, though some have powers not chronicled in the Known Worlds. Whether these powers are psychic, religious or demonic in nature even

Marcika has yet to learn.

Priest Durano Jorge Bursandra

Durano is one of the few Hazat who has earned a great deal of respect within the family despite not having much ability at combat. He heard the Pancreator's call at a young age and, rather than fighting it, his parents turned him over to the Church when he turned twelve. He slowly made his way over to Sanctuary Aeon and has become a noted healer.

Instead of being assigned to one area, as is the case with most priests and healers, Durano has taken it upon himself to travel throughout the Known Worlds, bringing his solace to the injured and soul sick on many planets. He currently hopes to start an expedition to the Kurga Caliphate, funding it with resources both from the Church and the Hazat. He hopes to bring peace, while his sponsors hope to learn more about their enemy.

Sir Juan Elabaro Hustin de Jericho

Despite the fact that the Hazat were among the last to recognize Alexius as their Emperor, the Hazat have been one of the house's which has most enthusiastically embraced the idea of the Questing Knights. Don Hustin is a prime example of this. His first major battle was the Siege of Jericho, in which the Decados and Hazat tried to destroy Alexius, and Don Hustin distinguished himself both in commanding a flight of space fighters and in boarding actions against Hawkwood ships.

Following the war, however, he found little to maintain his interest back on Sutek. Some said he was haunted by the deaths on Jericho and held himself partly to blame despite the fact that his engagements took place far from that moon. When Alexius made his calls for nobles to become beacons of hope, Don Hustin was the first Hazat to respond. Since then he has traveled widely, fighting Vuldrok raiders near one of their own worlds, stopping a slave ring operating from Aylon and rescuing priests from bandits. He has spent very little time in Hazat space but has become a symbol to a number of other Hazat who have either joined the Questing Knights or want to join.

Duchess Elena Cindias Victoriana Castenda de Sutek

In her early years, the leader of the Castenda branch spent almost as much time in Decados territory as on Sutek. Some say Duchess Elena's fondness for the mantis family comes from the wonderful times she had with them. Others imply that it is because of whatever blackmail the Decados got on her during that time. Whatever the case, Duchess Elena was a strong proponent of allying with the Decados. Since the end of the Emperor Wars, her interest in the Decados seems to have waned, however, and now she seems more concerned with extending the Castenda's power than in intriguing about the Emperor.

She has set her eyes on consolidating power on Sutek and extending it to surrounding worlds. One of her primary vehicles for this appears to be the Church. Near the

end of the Emperor Wars a "digestive illness" swept through the old Church leaders, killing off many of them. Those who took their place all seemed to have ties of one kind or another to the Castenda and to Duchess Elena. Duchess Elena has also begun to hold quiet meetings of Castenda leaders. All these meetings seem to coincide with what Sutek natives call the "dark moons", when both of the planet's natural satellites are obscured.

Marco Demano

Though not a noble, Marco Demano came to fame early in the Emperor Wars, when his resolve kept Prince Juan's legions from breaking during a Castenda counter-attack on Sutek. Most of the Hazat internal battles received little publicity, but Marco's stand occurred at a critical time for the Eduardo branch. Prince Juan had just established a foothold on Sutek and had landed most of his transport spacecraft. Had the surprise Castenda counter-attack succeeded, he would have lost much of his spacefleet. As his legions prepared to leave the field, Marco stood up, invoking numerous past Hazat heroes, and rallied the troops.

His exploits did not stop there. In one battle against the Li Halan, he personally lead the attack which drove the house from the field. The action which enabled him to leave the ranks of serfdom was the rescue of one of Prince Juan's nephews during a Hawkwood attack on Sutek. Already 35, and having served 20 years in the legions, Prince Juan gave Marco and his immediate family freemen status and land which Marco could pass on to his children. In the 20 years that have passed since then, Marco has become a leading member of the Estancia and travels frequently between Hazat holdings. He has quietly begun urging his fellow Estancia to keep a closer watch on those who hold power around them. While there is no way Demano could be thought to have democratic leanings, he has come to believe that something must be created to check the abuses of the noble houses, the Church and the League.

Roleplaying
Hazat Characters

- Thrill seeker: some Hazat have no motivation other than the next thrill — hunting vicious beasts, chasing pirates for pleasure or proving themselves the Known Worlds' greatest duelist.

- Combat addict: a little above (or below) the thrill seeker is the combat addict, who lives only to fight and fight again.

- Driven to lead: whether motivated by honor or glory, no few Hazat believe they are the only ones worthy of command. Everything they do is dedicated to confirming this belief.

- Holy warrior: The Hazat's proximity to Holy Terra

may well be the reason so many of their knights have become holy warriors, fighting for Prophet and Pancreator. Many join religious orders like the Brothers Battle, while others crusade on their own.

- Avenger: righting wrongs done to an individual or her family is an important part of the Hazat. The wrongdoer can be anyone from a relative, to another house, to the Emperor himself.

- Explorer: the Hazat like to go where no one has gone before and come back covered in glory. This can involve finding lost worlds, seeking out ancient ruins or visiting the deepest jungles in search of alien races.

- Glory hound: nothing matters as much as the renown which comes with great acts. One must carry out heroic deeds and be recognized for them.

Gamemastering Hazat

- A Kurgan dissident has made it to the Known Worlds, but Caliphate assassins are hot on his tail. The characters must protect him so that he can deliver valuable intelligence to the Hazat. Of course, the fact that he can block psychic investigation might leave many questioning the reliability of his information.

- A small family branch with close ties to the Castendas appears to be spending many moonless nights on Sutek in ancient ruins. Research reveals that the ruins have served as a temple for innumerable religions, and may have been first occupied by Sathraists. Are the Hazat worshipping there or using the cover of darkness for something even more nefarious? Are the characters going to risk revealing them?

- An impetuous young Hazat has been captured by the Muster while attacking what he thought was a slave base. In fact, the base was a mercenary training facility. The Chainers are especially upset about the number of their members he killed. What will the characters have to do to get them to release this hot-headed knight?

- A member of the Justus branch is seeking to make amends for what his ancestors did to some Ascorbites (sentient aliens from Severus) hundreds of years ago. He needs the characters to find the Ascorbites' descendants and give them several thousand firebirds. Only in this way will his honor be redeemed. Since the Hazat and Decados are such good friends, the characters should have no problem traveling through the worst parts of Severus...

- The characters discover that some Church land on Holy Terra once belonged to their ancestors. For some reason, the family was never notified about it and the land fell into the Church's hands. There may be some way for the characters to regain this fief.

Traits

Blessings

Natural Leader (+2 Extrovert when in command)
Nerves of Steel (+2 Calm when in combat situation)

Curses

Combat Lust (-2 Extrovert when in combat)
Power Hungry (-2 Calm when not in charge)

Benefices

Estancia (1 pt): Not only is your character a freeman, but he is a member of the most elite group of freemen in Hazat society. He could have earned or inherited this status, but either way, his voice is one to which anyone in Hazat society will listen.

Combat Drugs (1 pt): Your character has come into possession of rare and usually illegal combat-enhancing chemicals. Each dose can raise either Strength, Dexterity or Endurance by two points for one hour. After it wears off, the character will be at -2 to all rolls until he gets eight hours of sleep. Each point spent in this benefice gives the character five doses.

Afflictions

Addicted to Combat Drugs (2-4 pts): Like the Addiction affliction listed in the House Decados chapter, only the character feels the need for these drugs most strongly in combat situations. If she does not have the drugs then, her lack of confidence reduces her Calm and all her initiative levels by one during combat.

Pillar of Faith: House Li Halan

by Rustin Quaide

Erian Li Halan halted, staring at the ancient wreckage before her. Corroded metal glistened in the late afternoon light. The crashed starship resembled an ancient metallic dragon that had plunged to ruin from the heavens. Here it had stood, broken upon jagged granite in the midst of an old forest, a mute testimony to a forgotten war. Lichen engulfed the shaded hull, and great vines rose from the earth, entwining the space gift, attempting to devour it.

"What is it?" Brother Guissepe Alustro had called from below, still climbing the trail, still losing in his attempt to keep pace with his aristocratic companion.

"A lander of some sort" she called back, her voice falling to him like muffled leaves. "Equipped for war." Brother Guissepe Alustro sighed, wiping the perspiration from his face. This would mean, of course, that Erian would feel the compulsion to explore. Her overt seriousness as she scanned the area was offset by the elfin cast to her face and features: spry at times, aristocratic but moving with a graceful playfulness. The image of a cat came to Alustro's mind, hungry but strangely smug and satisfied. Here on Cadavus they had rested, she under disguise, lest her family, the proud and orthodox Li Halan, found her — or worse, the Decados, who might use her as a pawn in delicate power negotiations. She moved towards the ruined ship.

The afternoon light fell in slants through the great trees; the area about the wreckage hid under a canopy of autumn leaves. Distant bird calls and the sound of soft falling leaves reached Erian as she climbed towards a tear in the ship's side.

"Alustro, come here!" her voice commanded with effortless clarity. Brother Alustro, his mind wandering, contemplating the religious impressions of the situation, snapped to attention. He often contemplated the Omega Gospels, even during mundane tasks such as waiting for their Charioteer contact on this strange world. The guildsman would not meet them for a week, and they had heard rumors of old Second Republic ruins — which brought them here. Breathing heavily, he made his way to her side.

Erian brushed the metal side with her hand, rubbing with nimble fingers a dust-covered insignia. Gradually the insignia became lighter, a red rose against a field of five stars.

"The ancient insignia of the Li Halan" she whispered. "Even here, Alustro, the family finds me, in the debris of the past." There was no escaping her heritage, she mused.

"That is not the current symbol," Brother Alustro said. "Your sign is the Cross of Life."

"It wasn't always" Erian softly volunteered. "The ancient Li Halan, my ancestors, bore the Red Rose before our conversion." She climbed into the ship, moving through the torn portal. Alustro could hear her voice echoing within the hull. "My ancestors worshipped the dark powers, Alustro, from which we later repented, turning toward the light of the Pancreator." Alustro shuttered. He had heard such tales from his uncle about the old Li Halan. The noble family most devoted to the Pancreator and the Universal Church had once been infused with a demonic darkness. They were the terror of the Known Worlds. Even today, the old reputation followed them, an unwelcome shadow.

Erian moved through the ship. Pools of rain water and dampness greeted her, until she reached the pilot's cabin. There, with light falling through filtered windows, was a skeleton strapped into the pilot's chair. She looked closely, absorbing every detail. Remnants of black and purple clothing hung onto the frame, giving a scarecrow's appearance to the pilot's remains, but failing to hide the odd bend in the vertebra. The pilot had died on impact. The skull smiled, eye sockets staring through the filtered window into the forest, into nothingness. She noticed the pilot's insignia, the red rose, and above it, written in pre-Second Republic script, a name: Seng-Chih Li Halan.

"Hello, cousin," she whispered. Instinctively, she made the sign of life over his remains.

Brother Alustro climbed into the cramped pilot cabin. "Here's where he fell," he heard Erian say, as if to herself. "Seng-Chih Li Halan. He attempted to wrest the family from Lucifer Li Halan, the Prince of Morning. And failed. Rumors are that he fled to Malignatius and Cadavus, to stir up his supporters there. He was shot from the sky. Poor fool. The favor of heaven was not with him. Lucifer was too mighty for any upstart to bring down."

She sighed. The cries of lone birds echoed mournfully in the ancient ship.

"How long ago did this happen?" Alustro asked.

"Long, long ago. Before the Second Republic rose...see, he had reconstruction surgery for his lower jaw." Portions of the mandible looked reconstructed. The medical technology had been better then. The calcium infusions were only slightly discolored. "Better than today's, not as good as Second Republic surgery...Alustro, you must say a prayer over him. Administer the rites of departure." She wistfully looked about the cockpit. "You know, Alustro, when we saw the Gargoyle in the Nowhere Wastes, I thought it was an omen that I would discover my future. Instead, I discovered my past."

While Brother Alustro began his incantations, Erian rifled through the cabin, finding an ancient gun and a strange packet. Opening it, she unfolded an old map, covered in mathematical symbols and calculations. An old star map. A larger universe unfolded before her. What had preserved it so long? Ragwood content? Forgotten preservation technology? She smiled. Here were the gates to new territories, unfamiliar worlds. The future had waited for her, after all.

"It will be dark soon," she finally said. "Let us perform the rites for the dead and leave."

Introduction

House Li Halan, bound by oath to the Pancreator and by tradition to the Universal Church of the Celestial Sun, reigns supreme on the worlds of Kish, Icon and Midian, and the recently conquered League world of Rampart has added a greater technical base to the Li Halan fleet. Often feared and misunderstood by the other houses, House Li Halan holds the dubious honor of rising from the most decadent house to the most pious and orthodox within a single generation. This orthodoxy is tempered by a deep love for its subjects, and the subjects of House Li Halan are well provided for, rivaling House Hawkwood's social services on behalf of their people. Championing the Urth Orthodox power structure within the Church, they have been known to intervene on Church matters when they feel that radical elements threaten Orthodox dogma. The guilds and other houses have looked askance at the Church-Li Halan alliance. That House Li Halan once briefly placed a theocrat at the center of power on Byzantium Secundus has not helped their reputation.

House Li Halan is a house built on contrasts. Starting out as democratic champions of the people, the house now rules by hereditary decree. Their Oath of Servitude to the Pancreator has replaced one of the house founder's earlier oath to a preadamic demon. While the house desired to place a theocrat on the throne of the Known Worlds during the Emperor Wars, it eventually backed House Hawkwood at the urging of the Patriarch. Following the Church's teachings on the evils of technology, it seized the world of Rampart to protect its people from the dangers — and to gain a new technical base for it fleet.

"It is a house which bears study," wrote the Guild Historian Giotto. "Fortunately or unfortunately, we live in a time where their power is felt. To ignore them is to ally with them, yet to gain insight into their goals, one must understand them." House Li Halan has met and overcome many obstacles in its proud history. Surviving since the First Republic by force, intimidation, popular support, conversion and guile, it has built up from a desert world base to place itself among the five ruling noble families. Some say that its drive for power is not over.

History
Early History

The Li Halan claim descent from the Emperors of China and Japan, among other royal houses of old Urth including, according to legend, the Emperors of Brazil and Kings of Portugal, House Bourbon, House Roosevelt, House Stalin, and the Kings of Prussia-Greece. The first records of this remarkable family enter Diasporan history around 2600 as "Li-Halan Takeda," who owned vast interests in colonizing firms. A distaff member, Adriano, was given leave to oversee the operations on Kish, than called Escoral, primarily an iron-producing and nanotech world. The remnant threads of the First Republic were rapidly unraveling, and Adriano, as Governor, named himself Adriano I, Protector of Kish. Seizing the First Republic air fields and ports, he gained a sizable fleet. Elements within the planetary defense force were in his pay and allegiance, for local authority was replacing First Republic authority across the Known Worlds. Under Adriano and his son, Lucifer (Yasuo Nan-chen Li Halan), the world of Icon fell to the enterprising family.

The first Li Halan were democratically elected on Escoral, but held the monetary and military power, and were titled "First Citizens." Their power came from the people, and they openly solicited their support. They had rivals with two other wealthy families, the Verloren and House Tanaka. Various combinations of these families ruled Kish, usually with the Li Halan holding the upper hand. House Verloren was destroyed by an alliance of the Tanaka and Li Halan early on. However, since considerable marriages had taken place among the families, the descendants of the Verloren survive in the Li Halan. But even with their alliance, the rivalry between House Tanaka and the Li Halan endured for over two centuries.

It is with Lucifer the Sathraist that the reputation for the house's decadence began. Said to have sold his soul to dark powers to increase his conquests, Lucifer's reputation quickly grew. His palace, the scene of nightly orgies and reveries, frightened the populace by reputation. Sathraist practices were openly displayed. Lucifer Li Halan reached "The Vision Dark" by aid of various drugs and alien artifacts. There he found the demon which gnaws at time, and opened himself to it. The Compact of Lucifer bound

House Li Halan to the service of Pangeren the Thrice-Cursed, a dark being whispered at in Ur-Ukar mythology. The dark devourer, it was rumored, promised to grant House Li Halan long life in exchange for servitude.

Ironically, Lucifer's grandson, Lucifer III (also called Chung-shu), treated with the Prophet and let him preach on the growing Li Halan worlds. "The Message to the First Citizen" found in Galaxia 2:1 refer to the Li Halan. Zebulon said, "And when wisdom and darkness have had their fill, then the vessel yearns for light," and the First Citizen replied, "Go your way, Prophet, it will be long before I follow you." Later Li Halan took this verse to heart, while near-contemporaries claim that Zebulon and Lucifer discussed Sathraism with gentlemanly discourse.

Leonardo The Magnificent, Demonson

Democratic institutions gradually became replaced by the hereditary title "First Citizen" and then "Prince." Commoners were allowed voices in the lower assembly, while the upper assembly was composed of the leading families of Kish. It was Princess Cassandra who won Malignatius from the Free Traders. She was rumored to have taken an Ur-Ukar lover, and her son, Leonardo the Magnificent, was whispered to have little humanity in him. Yet Leonardo was fully human, despite the remarks of his fearful subjects.

Leonardo united the Li Halan with the other wealthy house on Kish, the aristocratic Tanaka, by slaying Sidiro Tanaka and marrying his daughter Aika. Inviting the Syndo-Anarchists and Red Orthodox leaders of Cadavus to peace talks, he personally slew the leaders of the waring forces and claimed the troubled planet for his own. Midian actually invited him in during a terrible civil war, where he allied with the Northern League against the Orthodox Unionists and took on the title "Protector of Midian." Leonardo was said to converse with ancient alien intelligences through preadamic technology found on Icon. Astonishingly beautiful, he lived for nearly two hundred years. Whispered that he sold off his soul in shards to various dark powers, he became known as The Patchwork Prince.

The Second Republic

During the Second Republic the Li Halan continued to hold great power on Kish, Midian and Icon. Although the nobility had lost most of its power, if not its titles, the Li Halan fared well. Keeping their titles, the family head reverted to the honorific title of First Citizen. The family maintained its wealth, possessing the majority of industry and banking firms on their main worlds. The President Pro-Council, the legally represented head of Kish, was usually one of the Li Halan family. Through the wise economic policies of Palides Li Halan, its vast wealth increased. The entire government became little more than its purchased players, and it held a tight reign on power.

Its decadent ways continued out of sight of the population. House rituals became important, and it began to solicit the Church frequently during this era. The policy of marrying into rival families continued during this time, albeit by more peaceful means.

Its main rival at this stage was the Blue Party, sometimes derogated to "Red Hands" by the aristocracy, to denote their labor in the fields. The Blue Party was a democratic reformism party, and originally anti-Li Halan. The Li Halan party, or "Green Party," was economic and socially conservative. After two centuries of extensive corruption, both parties belonged to the Li Halan, and their philosophies were indistinguishable from each other. Li Halan won as both Blues and Greens. Their most prominent foe during this era was Citizen Speaker Dior DuGhent, a reformist and "people's politician."

The Li Halan began to ally with the Church at this time for political reasons. A devout population often stayed clear of politics, or could be swayed to vote with the Li Halan. It also was the first family to purchase back its power from the overburdened Second Republic. Markain the Magnificent saw his chance when he paid off the central government for noninvolvement in Li Halan affairs. He was from the Midian branch of the family and assumed the family fortune when Chaparo and his two sons perished during a hunting accident on Grail (3796).

Combining the titles of "First Citizen and President Pro-Council," Markain titled himself "Prince of Kish, Icon and Midian and Lord of the Outer Hegemony." Malignatius remained longer in the Second Republic orbit, but the Li Halan were eyeing it like a ripe plum ready to fall. When the rebels struck Byzantium Secundus, the Li Halan fleet was among the Ten that shattered the Second Republic and paved the way for the Empire. During the chaotic years which followed, it retook Malignatius, but not war-ravaged Cadavus.

Conversion of Cardano, "The Shield of the Prophet"

Decadence and corruption renewed themselves after the Second Republic fell. Prince Tupal held "Demon Nights" when prisoners were hunted by the aristocracy. Kelniron the Cruel slew his twelve mistresses, each with a different poison, and spared or slew prisoners as the whim took him. Ustirin The Unspeakable took delight in masquerading as various preadamic gods and devouring his enemies. These, it was whispered, were the demons named in Ur-Obun and Ur-Ukar mythology, beings strongly condemned by the Church. "I have returned from the Li Halan court, and have a strong desire to bathe," wrote a Decados emissary.

The rumored Garden of Seven Pains was enough to break enemies of the house. Here, it was said, the human spirit itself was devoured by dark powers, producing an eerie melody which played on various wind instruments. The transfer of pain into art was the delight of the Li Halan artisans, who strove to create a culture of beauty from suffering. Princess Desiderdre dined there, attired as a swallowtail butterfly, while her attendants bathed her in flower nectar.

Throughout this period the general population was untouched, but rumors of the Li Halan's vile acts occasionally stirred up revolts led by educated reformers or peasant priests. The bishops of Kish were in the house's hand, but they were also the only effective voice of opposition as the democratic institutions gradually decayed.

Prince Rikard Cardano Li Halan, titled "The Red Demon," was the cruelest on the throne. He lead the Li Halan fleet into victorious battles against local barbarian incursions and rival house attacks. So great was his wrath that his own sons feared him. To contradict Cardano was suicide. The only joy Cardano had in life was in his mistress, Amorita, an artistic and educated woman of rare talent. She held great power, but was merciful and swayed the councils of Cardano. He could not deny her anything, yet she asked for little. When she spoke of her desire to join the Eternal Sanctuary (Amaltheans), his heart broke. To everyone's surprise, he let her go. Falling into a dark depression, he kept his own council ever after. Yet his taxes and tyranny finally brought on a rebellion. Lead by Aurelio Li Halan, a distant cousin, it gained support among the fearful military. Soon Kish and Icon were in the midst of civil war (4416).

Cardano brutally crushed the rebellion on Kish, hanging 6000 of the enemy on the streets of the capitol. He then turned his attention to Icon. Summoning his immediate family, he moved to Icon and took charge of the loyalist forces there. The skies were won and Aurelio's outside aid was cut off. Falling back into the Twerrid Mountains, Cardano pursued him with the relentlessness of an angry tiger. Finally claiming victory in the Valley of Skulls, he personally pursued Aurelio into the preadamite caverns. What happened next has been retold countless times across the Known Worlds.

The Li Halan historian Chalice II wrote about this historical event: amidst the preadamite ruins Cardano moved against Aurelio, leading his loyal forces. Defeating his kinsman in single combat, he moved to deliver the killing blow. Aurelio trembled, and clasped his kinsman's knees. Suddenly a voice, emanating with great authority, cried, "I call you to the Light! Empty your vessel!" A blinding vision of the Prophet brought Cardano, his family and soldiers, to their knees. Wave after wave of light shot through them, as they heard the divine voices of the Empyrean and beheld the Holy Flame of the Pancreator. Cardano wept with joy and, seizing his sword, smashed it on the rock, crying "We come at last! Forever after my house serves the Pancreator! The Curse is broken!"

Embracing his kinsman, he emerged from the cave a changed man. That same day his palace guard rounded up decadent cousins and kinsmen and sent them to monasteries. Church bells were rung. The banner of the Church

was flown from the Li Halan palace, replacing the bleeding rose of House Li Halan. The jails were emptied of Church members, and when Cardano returned to Kish he fell on his face before Bishop Aemlin. His immediate family, also witness to the event, were likewise changed. Aurelio was married to his daughter Sarah, and his younger son, Midenzo, joined the priesthood.

Next came the reforms. House Li Halan provided security, food and health services for all her subjects. House members swore oaths to faithfully serve the Church and people. Church education was open to all, and the University of Kish was founded. The military was updated, and sycophantic commanders were replaced by hardened captains of proven worth and loyalty. The Patriarch, Adrian IX, sent tutors to the Li Halan. Agricultural and economic reform followed, and the crushing taxes were lightened. While a benign autocratic rule replaced a decadent despotic one, democracy did not return. Instead, the subjects of the Li Halan could elect community leaders and boards to decide local issues, but the old assembly was but the mouthpiece for the Li Halan. While greatly empowering the people on local issues, the population could not interfere on the greater issues. The Church was also exempt from local law and taxation. The population welcomed the reforms, and grew loyal to their ruling family. With the Church-House alliance, there was no other opinion or option open. Cardano dropped the title "Prince" and called himself Head of House Li Halan ever after. He considered Prince a vain title, and the old title "First Citizen" again emerged, along with "Late Convert," a reference to the Omega Gospels. Some of Cardano's heirs have retained the title "Prince"; this has depended on the inclinations of the various house leaders.

Devoting his family to "the Heart of the Prophet," Cardano ensured that the Li Halan-Church alliance remained steadfast. "House Li Halan's conversion was a miracle," declared Adrian IX. The family tended toward strict Orthodoxy, and the Orthodox members of the Church trained the children of the house. In return, the Li Halan openly supported the Orthodox elements within the Universal Church. "More Orthodox than Orthodox" became their unofficial motto. The idea of a theocrat for the Known Worlds was first conceived after a meeting of Cardano and the Patriarch. The enemies of the Li Halan have long accused them of harboring this idea, a charge the Li Halan do not deny.

Amorita returned to the Li Halan court as an Amalthean. Cardano was overjoyed to see her, and she became his closest advisor, but relations between them remained formal until his wife, Chantel, died. Cardano finally got his wish, and Amorita and Cardano were wed before the Bishop of Kish. When Cardano died (4459), the Church alliance was unshakable.

Many interpreted the momentous events on Icon differently. Some state that Cardano and his family were struck by preadamic technology and their conversion was something akin to seeking an explanation for the unexplainable. Others claimed something infested them in the ruins. The more skeptical believe that Cardano allied with the Church for purely political reasons. A horrible civil war, brought on by taxation and the decadence of his house, left him with scant support among the population. Allying with the Church renewed the strength of the Li Halan, for Cardano realized that another such uprising might destroy him. The Church was popular with the peasants and this gave him a renewed support.

The more cynical state that the Universal Church engineered the Li Halan conversion. They hold that Amorita was a Church spy, and that by removing her from court, the Church engineered the Prince's eventual conversion. Within the ruins, they whisper, a defeated Aurelio handed Cardano a note stating "Embrace the Church and I shall return to you!" Below was the unmistakable signature of Amorita. Romantics of all shades prefer this version. Guild Historian Giotto wrote "Cardano's love for Amorita transferred to the Church she had joined. By unifying with the Church, the Li Halan leader psychologically sought to reunite with Amorita. Amorita was his crutch, which was replaced by the vast power and authority of the Universal Church of the Celestial Sun." All agree that the alliance between the Li Halan and the Universal Church is unbreakable. "Faith Is Harder than Steel!" has become a Li Halan motto.

Cardano's Heirs

Certain members of House Li Halan stand out after Cardano. Tristam "The Saint" Li Halan pushed agrarian reforms which gave each peasant his own family plot to till. Calchas "The Hermit" defended Icon against a heavy barbarian attack. Wearying of high office, he left the throne to his brother Torrin, and became a holy hermit on Icon. Princess Melissa (the mother of Flavius Li Halan) attempted to delve into the mysteries of longevity. Only an attack by the Engineers prevented her from acquiring the drug she needed.

Halvor "The Sword of the Pancreator"

The pinnacle of House Li Halan's power and authority came under the theocracy of Halvor (4690-1), often called "The Iron Patriarch." Halvor, the second son of Rinaldo the Pentecost, was chosen for a life in the Universal Church. He was a quiet, studious youth, learned in dogma. Becoming Bishop of Kish while quite young (24), he earned the recognition of the conservative powers within the Universal Church. There was talk that he might one day become Patriarch. His elder brother and Li Halan heir, Rajmund the Unready, fell in battle against the barbarians. A startled young bishop succeeded as heir to House Li Halan upon his father's death.

Grief stricken over his brother's death, Halvor began to question the divided authority of the Regency and Patriarchy. A strong believer in the idea of a Universal Theocracy, he began to muster his military and political forces. The combination of the office of the leader of House Li Halan and Bishop of Kish was unusual but not forbidden, although a few criticized the ethics of this. Most kept quiet, for already members of Temple Avesti attached themselves to Halvor.

Elected to the 10-year title of Regent, Halvor began to put his plans into action. The other houses backed his election to avoid the machinations of the Decados candidate and due to the diplomacy of his Hawkwood bride, Lady Avyryl. Halvor was still young and many thought him interested only in theoretical Church questions. "Our pliable, smiling candidate became a dragon of steel," Princess Masika Hazat later said. His backers misjudged the soft-spoken, serious man. Possessing the intrigue and charm of the earlier Li Halan, Halvor was now regent. Talk of a theocracy spread openly. Several reforms, mainly in stellar travel, occurred under his rule.

When Patriarch Wiold IV died, powerful forces within the Church pushed for Halvor's ascension to the Prophet's Kingdom. The royal houses and guilds didn't believe the regent would be so brazen. But a swift election (some say with great intimidation) among the Known World bishops and College of Ethicals placed Halvor on the Patriarchal dais. For the first time the offices of regent and Patriarch were united (4690).

Great fear seized the other houses and guilds. A Hawkwood advisor who urged armed revolt was found dead, the victim of the Avestites. Armed zealots swept through the cities of Byzantium Secundus, proclaiming "The Reign of the Theocrats has begun!" Striking swiftly, secret police rounded up opposition. The other houses, afraid to confront the Church and Li Halan, fell to squabbling between each other. Only the Charioteers raised their voices openly in defiance. A dread weight hung in the corridors of power.

Despite feeble opposition, Halvor issued "The Decree of Theocratic Succession," stating that the offices of regent and Patriarch would be henceforth combined, "for the Prophet's heirs shall be the guardians of the Known World, universe without end." As Patriarch, Halvor called upon the bishops to declare holy war on any house or power that dared to defy him. Within five months all opposition was crushed and the Royal Houses were in disarray without a shot being fired.

Six months after ascending to the office of Patriarch, Halvor chose to publicly unite the two offices in a coronation. His men swept into the regency council, and none of the representatives objected. An Engineer representative was killed on the spot for his part in an alleged conspiracy.

After offering prayers over the dead body, Halvor said: "Well, cousins, let us plan the long awaited day." Publicly

crowned, Halvor named himself "Theocrat Halvor I, Patriarch by Grace of the Pancreator and Regent by Grace of the Electors." For five months the Known Worlds, stunned, acquiesced to the studious zealot.

But five months later, while preparing a fleet to crush a small mercenary band gathering to oppose him, Halvor fell sick. Sweating blood and falling into raving deliriums (since named Halvor's Disease), he wasted away. Even with the best medical attention of the Amaltheans, Halvor died, withering in nine days from a powerful man to a shrunken, shriveled corpse. No assassin or poison was found, no man or order owed up to the deed. Many saw it as divine punishment for the sin of pride. Others claim that he died as penance for the earlier sins of House Li Halan. Once Halvor died, the spell of fear and indecision among his opponents was broken.

Halvor's allies swiftly proclaimed his young son, Constantine, Theocrat of the Known Worlds, but a combined Hazat-Hawkwood fleet appeared off Byzantium Secundus, threatening the Patriarchal Fleet. A new Patriarchal election was called, and Constantine resigned the office of regent. Ustir IX was elected Patriarch and Constantine was left leader of House Li Halan. Many feel that if Halvor had lived another five years, the Known Worlds would still be a theocracy.

Recent History

During the confusion and shifting alliances which marked the Emperor Wars, House Li Halan lost Malignatius to the Decados. The primary reason for the loss was that the Li Halan had amassed an armada for the invasion of Rampart. They seized the League world, but have since found it difficult to export their governing philosophy there. The local population, used to the freedoms of a frontier world, smart under the Li Halan reforms (some needed, some oppressive). Revolution is in the air, and the Li Halan secret police (the Hidden Martyrs) have their hands full.

Using the technology from Rampart to back their fleets, the Li Halan attempted to place Flavius Li Halan upon the Imperial throne. Receiving the blessing of the Church, House Li Halan's drive for the throne ran up against the lightning military victories of the Hawkwoods. Following the Patriarch's lead, Flavius declared the Li Halan for Alexius. Some believe that a secret deal was made where the Emperor would aid the Li Halan in the retaking of Malignatius. Others offer a darker view. If Alexius died or produced no heir, the Known Worlds would fall to a Church-Li Halan theocrat. The Church gained in the alliance by several concessions granted them, as well as having the Imperial ear. The Patriarch wanted a Universal Theocracy. House Li Halan would have declared for him (or alternatively, he for the Li Halan) but there was not enough support among the other houses. The memory of Halvor still haunted the Known Worlds.

House Culture and Ways

The Li Halan emerged in a Republic ruled by a closed hereditary aristocracy. During the New Dark Ages they were despotic dukes. This family, which began as merchant-governors of Kish, survived by skillful manipulation and intimidation. Its earlier customs, grounded in Republican ideas and decadent hedonism, have been lost. After its conversion to the Universal Church, Cardano Li Halan set up a strict regimen for the young family members to follow. This regimen has since become family custom and tradition. Although harsh, it has renewed the power of the family and produced devout leaders.

Young nobles from House Li Halan are instructed from birth by a personal priest. The priest's task is to guide the youth in moral conduct, study of the Omega Gospels and Church doctrine, history (both house and Church), arithmetic, writing, language and courtly manners. At age eight, boys become pages in the house of a near relative and girls are sent to be ladies-in-waiting to the House Matriarch and learn royal etiquette and custom. The page lives a spartan life, where he must read the Omega Gospels, pray and study battlecraft before preparing the breakfast table. From breakfast to noon he waits on his lord. After the noon meal he studies battlecraft. Instruction in courtly conduct, oratory and dance follows. Only after the evening meal does the page have time for himself. From age 11 on he observes military maneuvers, sometimes watching actual battles.

The page lives with a peasant family during his 12th year, to establish the house-peasant bond. This is often the page's happiest year. While he studies three days a week with his tutor (and his host's children, in some cases), he learns the hard tasks of the peasant as well as observance of the holidays (Concression Day, St. Palamedes Day, Reflection Nights). The following year the boy spends serving the Archbishop of Kish, Icon or Midian. Returning to his parents at 14, the boy has had military training, Church instruction, learned courtly manners and gained insight into peasant concerns.

Until age 20, the young Li Halan male may elect for training in law, philosophy, music, or Church doctrine, but the main emphasis is on leadership. The head of the household usually instructs his heir, allowing the heir to sit in on decision making councils early on. Since the conversion, the succession from father to son (or even daughter) has been smoother. Being a tight-knit clan has prevented the violent family wars of the pre-conversion period (with some exceptions). The greatest violence done in battling for the succession is usually done by distant family branches, usually on Icon.

Officially a man comes of age at 16, during the Rite of Flowers. Praying and fasting for four days in a Church, the young man emerges in a white robe, and gives the Oath of Servitude: "I am Li Halan. I take the Oath of Servitude, which binds me and my heirs forever to the holy name and presence of the Pancreator, reflection upon reflection, eternally, universe without end. Neither death, nor wealth, nor power shall break this oath, as I hallow myself to the Pancreator, universe without end. In the Pancreator's holy name I surrender my will, to do the work of the Pancreator as revealed by the Omega Gospels of Zebulon the Prophet. I am bound to the creative will while I take breath and beyond, to become a guardian of the fire, in reflected glory forever, amen." A bishop then annoits the heir with rose scented water, consecrating him. The family heir takes this oath in the Ur ruins in the Twerrid Mountains of Icon, where Cardano Li Halan swore the family to the Pancreator. Upon the death of his predecessor, the Li Halan heir also returns to these ruins to take up house leadership.

The Li Halan women are educated in ancient and modern languages, Church doctrine and dogma, courtly manners, dancing, mathematics and military training (age 15-18). Their physical training is not as difficult as that of their brothers, yet they undergo physical fitness (archery, fencing, beastback riding) training and learn military strategy. House Li Halan has twice been saved by powerful matriarchs (Melissa at the battle of Three Martyrs and Amaratsu at Corhejo). This has not been overlooked by the house rulers. Generally House Li Halan has strong patriarchal leanings, yet women are not cut off from rulership. Some believe that women had a stronger role in Li Halan affairs before Cardano's conversion. One custom from the house survives from before this time. On the night before her entrance to womanhood (age 16), three women take the Li Halan candidate into the Cave of St. Mater on Kish (on Icon and Midian, local sites are substituted when space travel is unfeasible). In a cavern lit by innumerable candles called the Chamber of Mysteries, the young candidate answers the questions given to her by an old crone, a middle-aged woman and a young lady. Afterwards, the young lady, now a woman, emerges from the cave in a blue robe, crowned with a laurel wreath. She is now expected to perform the ceremonial and personal duties of womanhood as she enters high Li Halan society.

Some hold that this custom dates from the days of Li Halan decadence, when pagan worship and customs were openly practiced. Candidates who have undergone the ordeal, while remaining quiet, state that the questions do involve the Pancreator's role for women. Occasionally the Church or reformers within House Li Halan have attempted to halt this ceremony, but it has survived all attempts to uproot it. It is believed that the ceremony involves elements of Church teachings mixed with more ancient wisdom. Only three of the questions placed before the candidates became general knowledge: "Whom does the water serve?" "What is the meaning of the Prophet's oak?" and "What words did Zebulon whisper to the waters?" Some state these practices are similar to the rites of passage practiced on Old Urth before the coming of the monotheistic, pre-Universalist religions. Court poets and philosophers have long debated this.

Traditionally, the oldest son or daughter is trained to rule, while the second son is groomed for a Church role, usually that of bishop or archbishop. The third son joins the military. The second daughter also joins a Church order, while the third daughter and fourth son can choose their own roles after they serve the house heir in an advisory role. Generally, a Li Halan noble is trained to be deeply pious. They have an aristocratic air which distinguishes them even from the wealthiest citizens of their worlds. Cool and aloof, they are soft spoken and courteous, using language (and their oratory skills) as a beautiful tool.

Taught to be respectful of the humblest peasant, they are encouraged to listen to the cares and burden themselves with helping them. On certain days the head of house Li Halan allows his subjects to petition him. Soft spoken words of kindness often cure an injured heart. Their craft of oratory is a means of control. The Li Halan treat it as a strict science, and this remains the most secretive branch of their learning.

Among the Li Halan, it is considered bad form to be too emotional. Speaking ill of the Church or the family in public is punishable. Loud clothes and foppish behavior will lead one to the remoter regions of power (Head Archivist of the Rampart Granaries). Rulership denotes responsibility. Disagreeing with the policies of the house or Orthodox wing of the Universal Church is punishable by banishment. Respecting elders and those in lesser stations is expected. Young lovers may talk, but public displays of affection (beyond holding hands while under a chaperone's watchful eye) is bad. For those with mistresses or "forbidden" lovers, the better kept out of the public eye the happier for all concerned. The family may make excuses in some matters ("Poor Mira, wed to that seventy year old second cousin when she was seventeen, let her find some scant enjoyment with her Latin tutor"), but the lover is expected to use common sense and discretion in these matters. Often the mere hint of scandal will lead to a house investigation and trial. Those lucky enough to curry influence in these matters should still be cautious.

Love of money is considered bad form, and while the house commands tremendous wealth, it does not display this too openly. Speaking slowly and cautiously about business matters is the way of the Li Halan, and large deals are often done at a slow pace. The family knows its business connections, and the family runs itself at times like a cross between a business and a Church order. Businesses on the Li Halan worlds follow the house's example, and off-world business people are often exasperated by how long a simple business deal can take. In many ways it is a closed economic system; house members sit on all the major boards on the Li Halan worlds and keep a careful eye on daily doings. The sin of capitalism, along with the sin of technology, is mainly reserved for the Li Halan family and their trusted servants and partners. Getting into

this closed circle of privilege can take years. Once inside, everything suddenly becomes accessible.

Dress and Behavior

The Li Halan follow a conservative dress code. In daily life even members of the upper nobility wear the grays, blacks and violets common among the upper peasantry. Simple and elegant, these garments are worn with hooded capes, distinguishable only by the house insignia. On ceremonial occasions red robes are worn over black bodysuits which end with a coif over the head, revealing only the face. These outfits resemble the robes of the Church bishops; again, the coif and family crest distinguish these from administrative Church attire. The pages wear green, young girls wear blue. White is reserved for Li Halan women, except as noted below, and finely created dresses of Rampart *gika*-worm silk enhance beauty while remaining within the bounds of taste. At times in the Li Halan history plunging necklines and body paints were popular; after the conversion smaller signs are needed to detect subtle changes in political climate, such as the style of shoes or gloves. Body armor tends to be dark, and even Li Halan military commanders dress austerely.

The leader of the house and heir-apparent dress in white robes, covering a white body suit. The white denotes purity and faith. A small red rose insignia maybe worn as a clasp, denoting loyalty. The family crest would be displayed upon the ring insignia. Complete black was reserved for mourning, green was worn by young lovers newly betrothed (a new tradition which began with the peasantry of Kish), and blue for a family member about to join a Church order or who was repentant. While this dress code is somewhat austere for a noble house, there exist small signs denoting wealth and prestige. The more white is worn the closer one is in relationship (by family or responsibility) to the Li Halan leader. Minor house affiliations tend to more blacks and purples. The richness of material and style of even an austere garment can tell much about the power and position of its wearer. And during the Festival of Lights, even the Li Halan may join the masked populace in elaborate costumes, displaying for one day their wealth and creative style in dress.

Rising in Rank

Rising in rank in House Li Halan depends on present rank and connections. House Li Halan itself is large, with many nobles on Kish, Icon, Midian and Rampart holding kinship, although only the immediate ruling family wields complete power. Still, a poorer branch of the house, born to a small estate on Midian, may rise by talent or connection. Attaching oneself to a distant cousin while young may pay off later, as may the display of administrative or military skills.

Generally, the succession is fairly secure, and can only

be challenged by a powerful member of the family (an uncle or cousin with authority) unless popular sentiment or powerful factions back an upstart. Revolution is not the best way to rise to power in House Li Halan. Even belonging to the least branch of the ruling family offers privileges. An estate of serfs provides for the table, and the law and Church will grant some leeway as long as eccentricities are kept within bounds. Before the conversion, anything was permissable, but now the Li Halan spy networks do report on the piety and orthodoxy of minor house members. The Church is always open for members of the house, as are businesses seeking to curry favor with the royal house.

Freemen have risen in Li Halan rank, yet rarely serfs (save the mathematical genius Sencho). Generally chosen for skills (engineering, military, administrative), freemen can rise to wield considerable influence. Sorto, advisor to Hadrian Li Halan, was a broom maker's son from Icon. Hadrian asked his advice on all manners. Fleet Admiral Hashi came from a fishing village on Midian (albeit his family had connections with the Li Halan as harbor masters). Hashi rose to the rank of First Admiral during the Emperor Wars. The military is a good way for advancement, as is the bureaucracy. Friends of the nobility, often from the peasant families which housed them as children, are sometimes honored. The title Tomodachi is given to those whose service denotes special merit. This title is not hereditary, but it does denote social rank on the Li Halan worlds.

Powerful patrons also promote their allies. The Church is open to commoners, although the top posts on the Li Halan worlds tend to be held by family members. Joining the Hidden Martyrs, the Li Halan secret police, is one path to power. Again, the top ranks are controlled by the Li Halan. Any commoner who amasses enough wealth or power will probably marry into the family, continuing the old practice of absorbing potential rivals. Freemen find power in local elections, and serfs serve on village and farm boards. Yet the exceptions of large social mobility are rare. The Li Halan tend to have the most stratified society of all the major houses, and have a stoic's eye about this. "The Pancreator has placed the peasant to till the earth, therefore that is his role."

The Head of the house is sometimes referred to as Prince or by the honorific First Citizen; other times as The Li Halan (denoting that he or she speaks for the entire family). The heir is titled "Heir Apparent." Brothers and sisters of the ruling Li Halan receive the title Duke or Duchesses, but their heirs do not necessarily inherit the title. First cousins and second cousins, as well as those who have held onto large holdings, are Counts and Countesses. More remote Li Halan are simply referred to by their names, often followed by their holdings, "Mosora Li Halan, Lady of Gessa Island and Ruler of the Setter Hills."

The Hidden Martyrs

Although the Decados Jakovian Agency and the Imperial Eye have the best intelligence networks of the Known Worlds, Li Halan military intelligence has improved during the past decade, and in general, the house's intelligence is reliable. Even the Decados know little about the Li Halan secret police, the Hidden Martyrs. The Hidden Martyrs report only to The Li Halan. A fanatical organization, thought to watch the political, cultural and economic conditions of the Li Halan worlds as well as gathering intelligence on house enemies, they are rarely mentioned by the house. When an agent is revealed, the Li Halan disavow any knowledge of him or her. The Hidden Martyrs are a shadowy group, sinister by reputation and brutal in outlook. Perhaps due to their fanatic religious beliefs, these elite agents have no history of infiltration from rival spy organizations or double agents within their ranks. Other spy agencies generally glean information on the Li Halan through disgruntled nobles and bribery/blackmail of various court personnel. On the few occasions when the Hidden Martyrs have combined their efforts with the intelligence network of the Orthodox Church, their capabilities were formidable.

Allies and Enemies

Noble Houses

House Hawkwood: House Hawkwood is seen as a temporary ally. The two houses have clashed in the past, and Hawkwoods are seen as upstarts by the Li Halan. Still, by supporting them, the Li Halan have increased the Universal Church's power in the Known Worlds. Some members of the Li Halan family want to overthrow Hawkwood rule and place a Li Halan on the Universal Throne. In the final analysis, the present alliance is a marriage of convenience. If another house must sit on the throne, then House Hawkwood is preferable.

House Decados: "They have not embraced darkness enough to win through to light," commented Hadrian Li Halan. The old Li Halan looked upon the Decados as crass imitators. After the conversion, they were seen as a threat, but only in recent times (with the Decados taking of Malignatius) has the long-smoldering enmity erupted again. The Li Halan want to retake their old world, and would like to see the power of the Decados crushed. They have attempted to sway the Church at times in condemnation of this house.

The Hazat: Admired and respected by the Li Halan (who have envied their tactics), they are granted the utmost respect, even when the two houses have been at odds. Some within House Li Halan believe that an alliance of the two houses could topple anything in its path. Still, in the game of politics, respect and admiration make for great allies and great foes, both. Being devoted to the Church, the Li Halan admire martial discipline.

House al-Malik: Traditionally close to this family before their conversion (with some marriage between them), this friendliness and cooperation collapsed upon the conversion of Cardano Li Halan. With regret (but to the delight of the Universal Church) the two houses became philosophical enemies. The Li Halan believe that the al-Malik desire a Third Republic, and hold them as a greater threat than the Decados. Still, politics make odd bedfellows, and the distance between the two families allows for some friendly contact. If the Decados remind the Li Halan of what they once were, the al-Malik are fascinating due to the polarity of views between the two houses. The al-Malik are viewed with a mixture of curiosity and fear, and it is believed that one day the family must convert or face battle.

The Church

Urth Orthodox: Excellent relations are the norm between House Li Halan and the authoritarian branch of the Universal Church. At times, the Li Halan have added their weight to Orthodox decisions, which many see as interfering with the Church. When reformers have lead the Church, the Orthodox have looked to the Li Halan for succor and as a bastion of Orthodox strength.

Brother Battle: The Li Halan maintain good relations with these military monks, although the secrecy surrounding the order and their desire to follow and fight among their own has made their use limited. Still, young Li Halan have joined them, rarely to return to the loyalty of the house afterward. Members of Brother Battle on sabbatical are sought as commanders by the Li Halan military. Unlike the Urth Orthodox, who are growing wary of the might of the military order, the Li Halan dream of bringing them in more under the Church's authority, and have tried at times to accomplish this. Many lesser sons of the Li Halan have lived out their lives within this order.

Sanctuary Aeon: These healers are held in high esteem by the Li Halan, although the Li Halan have sided against them in Church debates. Still, Amorita's role among their order is not forgotten, and there are large healing sanctuaries on Icon.

The Merchant League

Charioteers: The Li Halan recognize their value, believing that the Church should strengthen their ties to this organization. The Charioteers are a force the Li Halan must recognize, all the while holding their ideas in contempt. They would prefer Church trained/influenced Charioteers.

Engineers: The Engineers and Li Halan have come in conflict over a longevity potion (Lypee-55) being pro-duced on Kish. For philosophical-theological reasons, some within the house wanted immortality, a remnant of the pre-conversion Li Halan. The Engineers destroyed the production center of this drug, and this has lead to a fallout between the two. Many Li Halan believe that the Engineers perform vile acts in the Pancreator's eyes, but they envy their technical skill.

Scravers: This guild was once an ally of the old Li Halan. After the conversion the two parted ways, with misgiving on both sides. Recently, certain aspects of the old alliance have returned, and the two have begun to deal again as the Li Halan have built up their war machine.

Others

Vorox: Although the Li Halan are in many ways the jailers of the Vorox — keeping a close watch on who comes and goes from the Vorox homeworld — they are also their civilizers. It was the Li Halan who took up the task of "civilizing" the feral aliens once Second Republic anthropologists and cultural ministers could no longer perform these duties (due at first to budget cuts and then to the Fall of the Republic). While some malcontents among outsiders and Vorox alike deem that the Li Halan disciplinary methods imposed on the civilized Vorox government are too brutal, most are thankful that the house has helped to breed reason into the too-often manic brutes. Strong friendships and alliances have been struck by the clannish Li Halan and the loyal Vorox. Some Vorox find their way into the Li Halan military, where their loyalty is rewarded. Vorox veterans find settlements in special communities away from population centers.

Kurga Caliphate: Apostates who must be converted. Often the Li Halan project onto them a dark mirror of themselves. Followers of a wrong path (which nonetheless came from the Prophet), the Li Halan are both fascinated and repelled by them. They have urged the Church to convert them, if possible, foreseeing an eventual war between them and the Known Worlds.

Holdings

Icon

Icon was founded by a splinter sect of Urth Orthodox, who settled in the northern part of Ithica. Other religious groups soon followed, including New Style Muslims and the Brethren of the Stars (Xianists), who settled in the region of Famater (originally Fatima). Although the people of these sects converted to the Prophet's message, vestiges of the earlier religions remain and have intermixed with the rites of the Universal Church.

The southern region of Urtata holds a large population of later arrivals. Small farms and huge Li Halan estates dot Urtata. Many Ur ruins were found here. The population of the southern continent is conservatively Orthodox and looks askance at the strange ways of their cousins in the northern hemisphere. Surprisingly, many of the best artisans of the Li Halan worlds are found on the planet, and Urtata dancing and poetry have been mimicked on many worlds. The conversion of the Li Halan took place in the Twerrid Mountains on Famater, a place feared by the local inhabitants.

Kish

A desert planet, it was here where the Li Halan rose to power. Escoral is the capitol city, marked by the grandeur of the Prophet's Cathedral and the Li Halan palace. Most of the rural population work on the large Li Halan estates, or are small farmers huddled in the Greenswarth, the temperate region along the coast of the Rwellim Sea, south of the great deserts. The Greenswarth is the only agricultural region on the planet, save for the northern city of Calgirn (originally New Calgary). Desert tribes, the Ishwin Confederacy, live in the harsh interior. Tied to House Li Halan by blood and oath, they make the fiercest warriors of House Li Halan. Originally independent, their power was largely crushed by Cardano. Now the tribes have limited autonomy, many of them having become herdsmen. Yet there exists no violence between them and the other inhabitants. Li Halan rule is strong and the planet lives peacefully under their hand. Rural outbreaks of discontent are swiftly crushed, and little word of these has reached other worlds. The entire population is Orthodox in belief.

Midian

The homeworld of Patriarch Palamedes, House Li Halan was invited in to quell a violent civil war between the Northern League and the Orthodox Unionists. The Northern League dwelt in the northern region of Lyonesse. Descendants of free thinkers, small democratic townships and those seeking escape from the overcrowded First Republic, they were hated by the settlers of Zujan in the south, who were Orthodox believers. Ruled by small despots after the decline of House Alecto, the Orthodox despots of Zujan joined in an attempt to conquer Lyonesse. While they possessed the larger armies, the Zujan Union suffered from the higher technological development and hit-and-run tactics of the Northern League. However, after 11 years and a crushing defeat at the Battle of Vout, the Northern League appealed to the Li Halan for aid. The Li Halan crushed the southern despots and remained as lords of Midian. The Northern League they left largely alone, merely acknowledging a sworn oath to House Li Halan. Zujan they divided into large estates, despoiling the minor noble houses there, a few of which were assimilated through marriage.

Alone among provinces of the Li Halan worlds, Lyonesse remains governed by a democratic constitution. Orthodox belief finds more liberal interpretation here, and the Li Halan have never been harsh in their rule. That

is because the greatest scientists, weapon builders, engineers and doctors tend to come from this continent. The citizens are treated well and in return, they have been loyal, if somewhat resented by others. The two times that zealous reformers attempted to crack down on Lyonesse, they were met with resistance by those house members who worried that such censure would cost the house vital tech innovation. Lyonesse holds the weapon factories and manufacturing plants of House Li Halan, and the technicians from here supervise fleet construction in Zujan, at the Lextius shipyards. Ironically, the religious fervor which caused uprisings on Midian swept through the Orthodox populace of Zujan. Lyonesse, with its democratic traditions, remained untouched.

Rampart

This League world was seized by the Li Halan during the Emperor Wars to increase their technological base. Despite Li Halan reforms (often an attempt to civilize largely unruly frontier people), there are seeds of rebellion in the air. Small skirmishes between the Li Halan military authorities and "Leaguers" have occurred in the Nordrist region of the tundra world. The technology gained from Rampart has greatly added to the strength of the Li Halan fleet.

People

Social mobility on the Li Halan worlds stagnated after the fall of the Second Republic. A caste system gradually took shape, and it is now rare for a person not to follow her family's occupation. At the top of the system are the Li Halan and Church. Generally, the local planetary bishops are from the Li Halan family. The family is huge, and holds most of the top administrative posts. A deliberate policy of intermarriage with local rival families has left the Li Halan in control. This does not mean succession has always passed from parent to child. Before the conversion, cruel wars were waged between family rivals. After the conversion, succession has gone more smoothly, but different branches of the family have died out and been replaced. The current Li Halan are titled the Basquim Li Halan, named after their estates in Basquim province, Kish.

Behind the royal family and bishops huddles a small middle and merchant class, clustered in the great cities and outer suburbs. These are often government bureaucrats, small traders or mid-management types working for Li Halan-controlled industry. An intellectual elite composed of scientists, professors, artisans and writers rule a strange world between the middle classes and aristocracy. Generally clustered around the university in Escoral or in Lyonesse Province, Midian, they are a closed class, carefully watched and carefully provided for. They dress austerely to separate themselves from the aristocracy, although since the conversion, many Li Halan also dress austerely. Few dare to criticize the ruling house or Universal Church openly; ethics are debated instead. Certain questions are in and out of style. A few poets have written subversive materials, occasionally published elsewhere, but most enjoy their favored "ivory tower" existence and don't rock the boat.

The freemen compose the next class (the intelligentsia and merchants are included in this category). On Kish they are only 8% of the population (and the Ishwin Confederacy composes half of these), but there are slightly more on Icon (10%) and Midian (14%, most from Lyonesse). On Rampart the majority of the people belong to this class, and the Li Halan have been careful in adding more serfs there. The freemen class is hereditary on the Li Halan worlds. Serfs and soldiers who perform outstanding service are admitted to their ranks. Generally, freemen are proud of their social standing. Most freemen do not own their own land; they rent from noble landlords.

Beyond the cities exist the great masses of serfs, the agrarian workers, ranchers, fishers and dependent farmers who make up the vast majority of the population. Fairly conservative and orthodox in religious outlook, they can be moved with pent up grievances or when the government becomes too oppressive. Generally the Li Halan social care of their subjects combined with limited "village" democracy (carefully observed) has removed the danger of open rebellion. Li Halan benevolence to their subjects rivals House Hawkwood's. There have been peasant revolts from time to time, never to overthrow the royal house but to petition the government for grievances. They are loyal to Li Halan (the exception being the newly conquered citizens of Rampart). While Li Halan society is fairly immobile, it is just. Corruption among officials and even among the family is punished, so most serfs feel that justice is real (even if standards of living vastly differ).

Generally, the ruling house (Flavius and his near relatives) employ a household staff of over 700 servants. Serfs work their estates. The primary Li Halan family estates are in Basquim Province, Kish, and the Zujan continent on Midian, with many smaller holdings scattered across Icon. There is debate weather to place large family estates on Rampart. The citizens of Rampart, unlike those of Lyonesse, are not thankful for the protection of Li Halan rule.

The Li Halan have a large military, of whom serfs make up the largest class of the common soldiery. Serving well in the military can earn some the status of freemen. There is a large military presence on all Li Halan worlds. Military commanders are drawn from the nobility, with freemen serving as non-commissioned officers. Recently, General Ijiri formed a new military college on Escoral, with an emphasis on technical training. Long an admirer of the Hazat, he has instituted some long needed military reforms. General Ijiri is also reforming the command school for nobles

to understand current military realities. About 3% of the Li Halan military are mercenaries, drawn from the finest soldiers in the Known Worlds. Military intelligence has improved under Ijiri, who had to flush out Decados spies after the loss of Malignatius — not an easy affair.

There is little slavery on the Li Halan worlds. Some existed in Zujan province, Midian, during the rule of the tyrants. After the Li Halan seized control of the planet, most slaves were freed. Some still exist in Sanarkan, on the eastern edge of Zujan.

Personages

Bishop Xenos

Tall, gaunt and thin, Bishop Xenos of Kish is a cousin of Flavius Li Halan, and is in the line of succession. Quietly Orthodox, and not without a scholarly sense of humor, Xenos gets along well with the family. His passion is in strengthening and spreading the Orthodox faith, and he is a "hard-liner" in Church politics. Holding lands in the Greenswarth, he is open to opposition views in conversation, but convinced on the spiritual correctness of his cause. Xenos is also highly-placed in Flavius's councils, and it is whispered that the two of them run Kish like a well-oiled machine.

Xenos has a secret fascination with preadamite technology. He has sent small parties of his trusted servants across Kish, exploring. Holding a small cache of these items, Xenos justifies that he is merely holding them for the Church. He actually holds them in case the Emperor Wars return. He has not made a secret of his desire to see a Li Halan on the Imperial throne. Xenos also has large investments with the Scravers guild, and uses them to search for Second Republic technology. For political reasons, he would rather not have this well known. His weapons arsenal, kept under lock and key, is quite impressive.

Erelah Li Halan

The aunt of Flavius and sister of Melissa, she is the House Matriarch. Under her tutelage falls the training of all Li Halan noble women. She is old and thin, a strict disciplinarian. Yet a few reforms have occurred during her reign as House Matriarch. More women have the option of military training (a result of the chaos before and during the Emperor Wars), and she has resurrected the Cybele Tradition of the old Li Halan. This allows for some choice in husbands among the distant heirs. Her greatest accomplishment was in getting Flavius and Xenos to acquiesce in this act. Some suspect her largely loveless marriage to Hachima Li Halan shaped her views. She is plain spoken and lively (if somewhat eccentric and embarrassing to Flavius). She often brings up the glorious reign of her sister, Melissa, in the presence of Flavius.

General Ijiri Li Halan

A middle-aged man of average height and build, Ijiri resembles the ancient Li Halan in character and physical resemblance. Coming from a distant branch of the family ("The Midian Li Halan"), Ijiri joined the military at a young age. Beloved by his soldiers, he won several important battles in the Emperor Wars for Flavius. Even the Hawkwoods feared him.

Yet when the Li Halan accepted Alexius's claim, Ijiri lead the Li Halan contingent in the new Imperial forces, gaining the new Emperor's respect. Ijiri lost his younger brother, Michio, during the Decados taking of Malignatius. It is something he has never recovered from. To date, he will not speak to any Decados representative, and is part of the war party urging Flavius to retake the planet.

Ijiri lent his tactical skills to the taking of Rampart. Soft spoken but self assured, he is the leader of the Li Halan military. Training is strict, but Ijiri has gained the respect of the men. He has also studied Hazat methods. Ijiri wed his childhood sweetheart, Nara, and has a son, Takeo, in the army, and a daughter, Arial. On Midian it is whispered that Ijiri's branch of the family has the purest Li Halan bloodline. Detractors state that he is seeking to eventually overthrow Flavius. But Ijiri's conceptions of family honor and loyalty overrule any urge in that direction.

Roleplaying
Li Halan Characters

The Li Halan are a large family which encompasses many types. While many stereotype the Li Halan as "religious nobles," there is as much variation among them as among humanity at large. Individual members vary according to goals, inner beliefs and temperament. The image of fanatic plotters dreaming of restoring the theocracy is not the norm (although, unfortunately, there are some of these). In general, faith is important to them, although interpretation and expression of it vary from individual to individual. Some see comfort in the dogma made from Zebulon's teachings, others earnestly try to live the spirit of Zebulon's Gospel, constantly seeking to better themselves and help others. Here are a few character ideas for individual Li Halan:

- A high Church member, cynical and politically astute — a Cardinal Richelieu — advancing Li Halan interests through pragmatic politics.

- A young Li Halan captain who has fought in the Emperor and Symbiot Wars. He/she will be less provincial and more accepting of differences than others in the family, and less prejudiced against old taboos (the character may have fought alongside al-Malik or Decados comrades, or known "good" Leaguemembers).

- A vengeful housemember who lost lands and influence when the Decados took Malignatius, and who is plotting to recover the world or lost wealth.

- A younger house member who ardently believes that the Known Worlds would be better off under a Li Halan theocrat than the Emperor, and who is protected by the family and Church.

- A gallant swashbuckler, exiled from the Li Halan worlds due to a scandal, who believes in giving his sword to the right cause — an Errol Flynn or Musketeer-type character.

- A business-minded Li Halan with investments across the Known Worlds. This sort of character will be more friendly to the guilds and pay lip service to Orthodoxy.

- A decadent, rural Li Halan, who secretly believes the pre-conversion Li Halan were right, but who is under investigation by the house due to disturbing reports. Think of Poe's *The Fall of the House of Usher* or Peake's "Gormenghast" novels.

Gamemastering Li Halan

Examples of possible dramas involving the Li Halan include:

- Spying out conditions on Malignatius, passing plans to pro-Li Halan factions there, or attempting to spy on house enemies on Rampart.

- Attempting to aid a disinherited family member against his/her usurpers

- Searching preadamite ruins for relics, or guarding such a relic which the house is giving to the Patriarch, one of unknown power wanted by many factions. If the Emperor takes an interest in the artifact, conflict between the Imperial Eye and the Li Halan secret police, the Hidden Martyrs, could break out.

Traits

Most Li Halan of the younger generation know something of the art of fencing and martial arts, since General Ijiri's reforms have begun to affect noble training.

Blessings/Curses

Church Standing

These traits affects how members of House Li Halan assimilate with the Church, a very important factor in house politics. It is rare for a Li Halan noble to encounter Church criticism publicly. Privately, however, erring members often find themselves critiqued.

Blessing

Virtuous (2 pts: +2 Impress among the faithful)

Curses

Doubter (+1 pt: -1 Charm among the faithful)
Penitent (+2 pts: -2 Impress among the faithful)
Apostate (+3 pts: -3 Charm among the faithful)
Intolerant (+2 pts: -2 Calm among the faithless)

Intangible Mountain: House al-Malik

by Rustin Quaide
with Phil Brucato

Sharzad al-Malik bowed low before the Shaykh Throne, glancing at the inscrutable face of Duke Hakim al-Malik. His sentence had awaited the duke's pleasure, and the lord finally emerged from his morning war council, ready to dispense house justice. Sharzad was accused of openly fraternizing with the Decados enemy. In the third year of the Emperor Wars, the crime carried a sentence of death. Outside, dark clouds loomed like angry demons over the Murruwah Palace, overlooking the great markets of Istakhr.

The young man swept his black curly hair aside with a brief motion of his hand. They are studying me, he mused, breathing slowly. A chime struck. An old man coughed, then all eyes were upon Sharzad. He stood awaiting judgment.

"Sharzad al-Malik, you have been witnessed on Leagueheim in the company of one Derrico Decados," read the Duke's young Vizier, Uljaytu. Sharzad lifted his head, glancing at the older qadi and advisors.

"It is the truth," he replied. Sharzad sensed the heaviness in the still air. The duke's powerful face betrayed no emotion. His brown eyes caught the reflected red light of the palace crystals, and sparkled with veiled menace. Behind the fluid red ocher of the hanging carpets, Sharzad felt whispers. "Is he so stupid he cannot climb The First Mountain, but must declare himself openly on jumpgate travels?" he imagined Duke Hakim's advisors murmuring. "Reprimand this foolish youth!" Behind neutral glances and the rustling of state papers, every soft movement, every sweep of an elder's robes took on a terrifying significance.

Duke Hakim clapped his hands twice, and the court fell into complete silence. The powerful bearded ruler appeared calm and dignified, as if he were judging a poetry recital. A soft whistling sigh escaped his lips. "Young cousin," his voice began softly, a kind undercurrent to the room's tension, "please explain yourself. I have reports here of gambling and drinking with this Decados noble. This is fine in normal times. Yet you declared your identity openly; rather unconventional. You jumped right into the Decados net. And the cream of our youth are dying, fighting off their repeated attacks, while we await for Hawkwood reinforcements. We are

at war, young cousin, not a celebration. Your behavior is very forward and uncomplimentary." His soft eyes hardened as he rolled a pen absently between his fingers.

"Yes, I drank and laughed and gambled and whored with Derrico while our forces were dying," Sharzad said in a strong, clear, voice. "I did not avoid him but sought him out. For men who are drunk relax, and reveal between jests valuable jewels normally withheld."

Duke Hakim arched an eyebrow. Two elderly qadi, used to a life of judging, exchanged furtive glances. "Pray, continue, cousin," Hakim said, emphasizing each word with the force of thunder.

"I was sent to Leagueheim to confer with the guilds, as an advisor to my uncle, Arrat," Sharzad said. "My mission was valuable to the Decados intelligence. In order to lure the thief from hiding, what better way than to place the gold in daylight? I deliberately ran up gambling debts, and Derrico came to help out a fellow noble — so he claimed. I played along. You see, great and noble cousin, I am trained in the Path of the Grape."

The duke laughed, and then his advisors followed. It was a legitimate path, but little practiced by the al-Malik. Still, immunity to alcohol was useful. Clearly the young lad was smarter than he appeared, mused Hakim, staring thoughtfully at his gold and crimson slippers.

"Pretending to give information while married to the cup, I gathered it," Sharzad continued. "Always Derrico pressed me about Malignatius, what we thought of the planet and the Li Halan claim, what we knew of its defenses. When seven toasts had occurred, my friend informed me that the Decados buildup was true, and began telling me what he had heard of valuable real estate on the planet. Great cousin, the Decados will attack the Li Halan world in a month's time."

Silence. Hakim folded his hands under his chin, as he smiled. "Excellent. Is that all?" Outside the vast windows, Sharzad could see the pointed spires of his city, Samarkand, an army of spears below flashes of lightning.

"No, great cousin," he said quickly. "One night, my good and

true friend worshipped the grape to excess, and fell prostrate before her. I took the liberty to ensure that his noble personage was all right, and picked up his banking records, to save them from the drenching liquids which covered his finery." Sharzad produced a small think-machine, handing it over to a guard. "It is interesting that one of Derrico's accounts is attached to the worthy name of Uljaytu. But I must be boring you with my tales of indulgence, which should not be brought up before the rarefied and learned court of my great cousin, may the universe honor his name."

With a swift motion of his hand, the duke summoned his guards to action. Seizing the young vizier, they dragged him off to echoing shouts of protestation. For a moment, Duke Hakim wondered what else his young cousin had learned out there. "Clearly you have our permission to follow in the Path of the Grape," Duke Hakim said, and dismissed Sharzad.

The next day the lifeless body of Uljaytu, formerly Vizier to Duke Hakim al-Malik, hung in the marketplace. All remarked on the richness of the clothes, and shook their heads. "The follies of youth," they said.

History

You know, my daughter, it is a rare thing for a man of high station to speak the truth, let alone recognize it. The higher in station he is, the more he spends to make the truth fit his desires, for it embarrasses him, like a beggar at his fine banquet. Many people, specializing in reading the unsaid desires of the powerful, have grown rich by pressing the truth into the favored wine of the ruler's temperament. They become his eyes, and he pays them to see, but they do not report with clarity. Better to have a dog's eyes than a man's see for you. But in a moment, a single rarefied moment, even a man of high station may glance at the poverty of his shadow. His shadow's very existence accuses him. 'See?' the shadow says, 'I go naked while you wear rich clothes. And for all your riches, I, who am closer to you than your beloved son, have not even one trinket to carry.' The early al-Malik, it was said, learned wisdom from their shadows. That is, they were all mad. Madness alone, daughter, shatters the illusion and allows us to see the unformed face of the mountain before the sun strikes it.

— The sayings of Tahir al-Malik the Doomed

Munir ibn Tarif (2586?-2665) was the greatest genius of the First Republic. He developed the Lukos Retina, which, when injected into the human eye, produced visions of the future. Created as a safety device for space pilots against the lure of Sathraism, Luktin-76 (as the visionsynth became called) also produced horrible addictions. Seized by the authorities of the dwindling First Republic for their own use, the initial benign effects of Luktin-76 were lost as inferior minds attempted to direct the visions into staving off the collapse of the First Republic. Visions, often cloaked in symbols and metaphors, did not produce the desired effect, and Munir ibn Tarif fled the First Republic, finding sanctuary with the Bashshar Corporation. The al-Malik can claim descent from him, although their claims to ancient Urth Persian,

Arabic and Israeli royal houses are unproven and dubious at best.

The Bashshar Corporation, which rose in prominence in the field of communications and weapon technology, made its mark in the declining days of the First Republic. Selling its high tech weaponry to both the Republic and their noble enemies, the corporation relocated from Terra to Criticorum for tax purposes. After the loss of New Istanbul in 2600, the First Republic's collapse accelerated, and the corporation's leaders desired stability. Lured to Criticorum by House Koprul, the corporation soon became the dominant power on the planet. Munir ibn Tarif was given a royal dwelling and private laboratory. There he developed the psilaser (later used by Lucifer Li Halan's troops to devastating effect) and seraphimiun, a synthmetal used in the construction of starships. It is recorded that Tarif was a master of genetic coding, mathematics and music. He sought to combine the three into one discipline, but the failure of Luktin-76 haunted him.

Tarif sought to rectify this by producing a newer visionsynth, Luxdei-3. Trying it on himself, he saw the flickering death of the stars before civilization reached its potential. He took drastic action. Moving his vast wealth to various holdings, Tarif fled with his supply of Luxdei-3, leaving family and fortune behind. Twelve years later, he was found on Istakhr, wed to a local woman, with two sons. Refusing all pleas to return to Criticorum, he died on his adopted world. Legend has it he walked out and was taken up by a desert storm (some say he was taken by a raging river during a flood), after hiding his supply of Luxdei-3. "I go to dance with the powers of Hell and break them," he is rumored to have told his elder son, Lufti, before his final departure. "The Path of Tarif" has come down in house history as the mystical/evolutionary path of the al-Malik. Yet those who know most about it say the least, claiming it is a universal goal for all sentients. "The Golden Steps of Tarif are hard by necessity," is an al-Malik saying.

Munir ibn Tarif's daughter from his first marriage wed Kansbar Caspari, President of Bashshar Corporation. The corporation eventually seized political control of Istakhr, which was devastated after years of clan warfare between two mighty houses, the Aswad and Hashim. Tarif's line from his second wife went from his eldest son descending to his granddaughter, Almira (2647-2723), who wed into the al-Malik clan, wool traders and interstellar merchants. Almira passed on to her descendants the secrets of Munir ibn Tarif's final insights, using memory and oral tradition to preserve what he had taught her. Thus, the al-Malik became the carriers of the seed of his far-seeing mind, desiring the uplifting of humanity with complete inner control over the calamities of the soul. The al-Malik, under Almira's influence, became "scientifically mystical" as later family members liked to tell. While many family records have been lost, the al-Malik can recite the roll of generations to the founder. For 600 years the al-Malik dwelt on Istakhr, noted for the superiority of their wool

(genetically designed), and their occasional prominence in market affairs. Their fortunes rose and fell, but they became a sizable clan.

Arif Abdul Salam al-Malik the Faithful

The first family member of note was Arif al-Malik the Faithful (3390-3480). He led his family commercial interests until age twenty-two, when he went alone at an inner calling into the Istakhr Desert. There, he claimed, the will of his ancestor, Munir ibn Tarif, was revealed to him in three days and nights. He returned two years later with the Lover's Calling, a series of revelations he delivered in the marketplace. Calling upon his listeners to cast off of the chains of prejudice and ignorance, he gained an immediate following, named The White Dancers (or *mawla*) by historians. Revealing to them the oral traditions of his ancestor, he lead them in purifying exercises to cast off "the old way." Tarif's teaching mixed with ancient esoteric traditions, producing a small sect of devotees.

It was during Arif's "Shaprut Exile" (3407-9) that he wrote *The Democracy of Wind and Stars*, calling for a universal parliament representative of all the Known Worlds. This work was instrumental to the various corporate interests, who slowly began organizing the Second Republic. Looking back to the 19th and 20th century democracies of old Urth, as well as the social arrangements of various alien and shamanistic societies, Arif called upon the duty of every sentient to fulfill its potential. This struck a chord with the spirit of the time, for already Galdwin's *Synthesis of Destiny* and Morrif's *Parliament of Will* called for a republic to replace the fragmented state of interstellar humanity.

Some called Arif a religious figure. This he declined, stating that Zebulon's teachings were enough to nurture a thousand future religions. He was but an awakened man, following "the Path of Tarif." The local authorities, lead by Nawar Caspari, feared him. Twice she sent assassins after him; both times, the assassins converted to Arif's vision. Finally, Arif lead his followers into the Istakhr capitol, Samarkand. The masses followed Arif. A few shots were fired by frightened authorities, but by day's end, Arif held the capitol. To the applause of the people, he declared himself the First Representative of the Universal Republic.

The Bashshar holdings on Istakhr fell into his hands. Nawar Caspari, the "Flower of Criticorum," came to the victor, expecting death. She fell back in amazement when he called her kinswoman. "For while the elder line of Munir ibn Tarif inherited the powers and riches of the universe, the younger line grew up, wool merchants, among the people. Now, kinswoman, will you not reunite the scattered seed of our distant father?" Nawar suddenly gained insight into Arif, and she answered that yes, she would rule by his side. Thus the al-Malik became rulers of Istakhr as well as leaders of the vast Bashshar holdings. The republican ideas of Arif al-Malik spread, and he used the vast wealth at his command to begin schools, start universities, perform public works and set up republican foundations to increase the ideas of universal democracy. He was a curious man, much revered in his lifetime, elected President of Istakhr six times and finally voted the title of "Duke"(*amir*) by the population. Amir had connotations on Istakhr as "Protector," a title he held the last two years of his life. The idea of a Second Republic was nearly universal at the time of his death.

Azhara al-Malik, the Flower of the Second Republic

During the Second Republic, the al-Malik were often representatives for their worlds, when not diverting their energies into their merchant empire. The Bashshar Corporation was absorbed (along with several other al-Malik corporations) into Monlux Stellar Technologies, which produced Terracite, used in Second Republic construction. It was at this time that the al-Malik reputation as a large merchant family began. Supporters of republican ideas, their good works and charities earned them a benevolent reputation. They remained hereditary Dukes of Istakhr, yet the family relocated to Shaprut, where they had many holdings. Called the Second Shaprut Exile (3691-4460), it saw the solidification of family power on Shaprut and Criticorum, while more distant relatives remained on Istakhr, little influencing events there.

Azhara al-Malik, a duchess of much learning (3670-3768), pushed the barriers between objective and subjective art in her studies, discovering innate powers of prophecy. These, she claimed, were genetically coded in her family by Munir ibn Tarif. Exploring the "Potentiality Pathways" as she called them, she came to an alarming conclusion. She redirected her wealth into areas which struck her family as odd, but proved to be wise in centuries to come. Azhara beheld the Fall of the Second Republic. Feeling it was inevitable, she urged drastic action. Asked if the Republic could be saved, she told a senator that there was one way. He returned the following day to hear it. The ninety-eight year old woman had died an hour before. In a gift wrapped box addressed to the senator were some common garden seeds and the note: "Plant deep for harsh winter." Some within her family remembered her warning, and when the nobles destroyed the Second Republic, the al-Malik hid various senators, politicians, philosophers and partisans from harm.

Some called their court of refugees "The Third Republic" as an insult, but the al-Malik took the title with pride. Banding together with the corporations and politicians which had survived the noble seizure of power, the al-Malik-League alliance began. In those times, each kept the other alive, for the heirs of the Second Republic had many enemies. Some al-Malik troops took part in the attack on Byzantium Secundus, to free it of rebels, and to the shame of the house, at least one prominent family member was

a·s

present when the Ten struck down the Republican institutions.

Rahimat al-Malik, the Lion of Shaprut

When the New Dark Ages descended upon the Known Worlds, the al-Malik consolidated their power on Shaprut and Criticorum. Yet their power was fading fast. Smaller noble houses (the Ghaiji and Dandin) undermined their authority on Shaprut. The Scravers became a real power, and vast parts of the economy fell into their hands. Decline was everywhere. Their republican ideas seemed antiquated, and civil strife rocked the house. Into this chaotic time Rahimat was born (4332-4414), a second cousin to the house's ruler. Seeking wisdom among the relics of the Second Republic as well as alien races, he came across a curious discovery. Among the surviving al-Malik on Istakhr, often little better than rural nobility and cattlemen, there were those who possessed the oral tradition, verbatim, of the much-vaunted Tarif. Those who remembered were from lesser branches of the family.

Rahimat al-Malik studied all the lore he could before going to climb the Two Mountains, a path he would not reveal immediately to his followers. The Way of the Three Mountains (or Bay'ho len Itka Tu) was first attempted by Arif, but was clearly present in Tarif's hidden code, Rahimat later revealed. Nonetheless, it was he who first brought the idea to the al-Malik as a living philosophy. When pressed, Rahimat admitted that the Bay'ho len Itka Tu had always existed, and was expressed perfectly in the poetry of Ban'on Be'n Kilou, a 25th century poet. The basic idea of the Way is that creation is, in fact, the Pancreator incarnate. The Way teaches respect for all things, but has a cold, merciless side to it as well. Since all things are one with the deity, nothing is truly evil or good. All things simply are. To become an enlightened noble, one must experience the many facets of creation.

Returning to Shaprut, Rahimat used his family connections to build a vast fortune, seeing to the day to day operations of their holdings, and skimming a fortune in the bargain. Working in the Shaprut Palace as an accountant, he slowly converted the staff of the impenetrable fortress to his way of thinking. One day, he threw Duke Sohrab al-Malik out the palace doors, and few left with him. Yet the duke had his resources, and his retainers came with armed troops. Leaving the palace to his partisans, Rahimat made his way into the planet's interior. After raising an army of disciplined followers, he struck. In a series of military maneuvers known for their brilliance, he destroyed the al-Malik armies in one year. Duke Sohrab al-Malik was slain, and Rahimat declared himself duke. Thus the lesser branch usurped the ruling branch (called the Curse of Nawar).

Rahimat made lasting reforms. He taught the oral traditions to the family, while creating the beautiful language of metaphors now employed by the al-Malik in daily speech (now known as The Graceful Tongue). The Way of the Three Mountains was presented to the al-Malik nobles and the worthy. He enforced spiritual and mental exercises, and declared that the Third Republic was in all hearts. Physically imposing, Rahimat could endure great suffering. After two years in power he allied with the Dandin against the Ghaiji, and then proceeded to destroy the Dandin in the hour of victory. "A wolf does not like cats in his den," he said. Next, alarmed at the power of the Scravers over all aspects of Shaprut, Rahimat infiltrated them with his own assassins, slaying their leaders. After two years, the Scravers, decimated by Rahimat's power, withdrew. This was the only time the al-Malik ever warred with any of the League.

In 4460 he seized Istakhr in a sudden attack. Wiping out the native Cestmir royal house (save the poet Lysander), he returned the al-Malik to their old world. "Istakhr was a beautiful woman with the marketplace for a dowry," he boasted. "How could I refuse her?"

Near the end of his reign, Rahimat survived an alliance of disinherited nobles arrayed against him, retaking Shaprut in a bloody battle. After this, he left the rule of the house to his son, Nadir. He left, "searching for the Third Mountain," and never returned. Rahimat's traditions changed the court, for he brought in seers and wisdom teachers. Even his enemies acknowledged his wisdom. The poorer al-Malik of Istakhr, reduced to rural gentry at best, suddenly saw their fortunes rise. Rahimat had wed a distant Istakhr relative, Zubeida, and shifted the balance of power within the house. Yet the departure of his strong presence left the family in disarray. For a generation, no strong leader emerged.

Asim al-Malik, The Sword of Istakhr

Rahimat's grandson rose with the wealth of the Istakhr Marketplace at his command, making the al-Malik the wealthest of the royal families. Gathering his forces, Asim attacked Aylon, held for the regency by the Keddah. From there, he gathered a sizable al-Malik/Merchant League fleet and seized Cadavus (later lost by his son, Kurush — along with the jump coordinates from Aylon). Finally, in 4490 he attempted to conquer Byzantium Secundus. The other royal houses feared a restoration of the Republic. Coming up against the Hazat-Regency fleet, he met his death off Pyre. The remnant of his fleet regrouped at Criticorum.

Tahir Majnun al-Malik the Doomed

The third son of Manara the Thrice-Cursed, Tahir (4530-4593) was a born warrior. During his youth, while climbing the First Mountain, he entered the ruins of a preadamite race on Nowhere. There, gazing at the alien architecture and symbols, he beheld a vision. All things

were energy, and all energy devoured lesser energy in a constant cycle. One by one the stars went out, and entropy devoured the universe. Tahir still stood, naked and alone in an abyss. He realized that by consciously sacrificing a small piece of his life force, he had avoided complete annihilation. Opening his eyes, Tahir saw that he was again on the howling sands of Nowhere. No ruins existed. Convinced that he was given the last key to Tarif's Path, he returned to court. Also convinced that the void beyond the devouring energies sought him as a lover, he named it al-Mannat, claiming that it was a female force which sought him. Ever after, Tahir spoke of Reunion with the Lover.

Sarraj al-Malik, his brother, died in 4548. Although young, Tahir had gathered a force on Aylon. Seizing the Istakhr palace, he proclaimed himself duke, slaying his brother Ahmad. Initially opposing Vladamir's claim to Emperor of the Known Worlds, Tahir struck with his own force for Byzantium Secundus. Winning astounding victories, he was finally betrayed to House Alecto by a Justinian spy. Vladimir spared his life, and Tahir pledged his support.

Granting land and tax reform, Tahir was initially popular with the people. He began the vast reorganization of the Istakhr Marketplace, which increased the royal coffers while adding protection for the Merchant Fleet. Tahir instituted the Mutasih, combining several market public and policing agencies into one. The Mutasih eventually became the al-Malik secret police, for much could be learned from the Istakhr Market.

Yet Tahir, haunted by his vision, desired reunion with al-Mannat. He saw her in the form of his sister, Kahana. He wed her in secret, but finally revealed the union before his people. They produced a son, Zahid, "The Dark Pretender." Tahir sometimes referred to himself as "Rasul al-Mannat", the Messenger of al-Mannat.

Elements within the army, lead by the vizier Faysal, revolted. Putting down the rebellion, Tahir saw his victory as a sign of grace from the Beloved, and had his artisans create a statue of al-Mannat on the spot. Writing down his esoteric beliefs, he finally practiced them in the open. Sacrifice was demanded to feed the darkness between the stars. This, coupled with his radical attempt to change the Graceful Tongue and teachings of Zebulon on al-Malik worlds, produced another revolt. Ja'far ben Sinhijah al-Malik, the last heir of the old Criticorum family, struck.

Tahir's forces were augmented by Ur-Ukar. Despite the larger army, Tahir lost at Mu'tasim Field. Escaping from the wreck of battle, he maneuvered his ship to the jumpgate. He never emerged again, and his last words to his loyal follower, Khalid, were "I go to greet the Beloved in the darkness between the stars." Most believe he joined her. Despite his evil reputation, his policing and economic reforms were long lasting. His son fled to House Decados and perished attempting to retake the throne 12 years later.

Recent History

The Criticorum branch of the family, after an initial burst of creative energy (reflected in the arts), fell into a slow decline. Eyed by their enemies, the al-Malik barely held their own. Power fell into the hands of the viziers and generals, while the royal house became remote. Finally, a formidable woman, Al-Abbasah "Claudia" Al-Malik (4803-4869), the daughter of a royal exile, seized control. Growing up on Aragon, a Hazat world, she studied their military methods. At age 24 she led an expedition of al-Malik exiles and mercenaries. After seven months of civil war, she seized control from Duke Sufyan al-Malik. She did not kill him, but forced him to seek the Third Mountain. He died in exile on Kish seven years later. Al-Abbasah wed his nephew, the gentle Tiraz al-Malik, an expert in agriculture. She reformed the military, and once again the al-Malik were a force to be feared.

Jabir al-Malik the Golden

Al-Abbasah's son, Jabir al-Malik the Golden (4850-4940), ruled over an age of learning. Revising the tax code, he began the Diwan, or land tax. Great public projects were instituted under his rule, and the schools and universities flourished. An intellectual man, the later half of his reign was marred by the Symbiot Wars, which ate up much of the treasury, and squandered al-Malik might in a long drawn out struggle. His great public charities gave him the title "The very saintly Jabir of Golden Memory."

After his death some of the family reverted to decadent ways, yet his grandson Duke Hakim al-Malik continues to hold a strong centralized rule. It was his misfortune to be ruler in the time of the Emperor Wars. The wars, coupled with the Symbiot Wars, drained al-Malik military strength. At first there was talk among the house of declaring him Emperor, but the al-Malik swiftly backed Alexius's claim to the Universal Throne. There were a number of reasons for this. Duke Hakim believed that the best way to form a Third Republic was by consolidation under an Empire first. Also, Hawkwood forces mainly held Stigmata, which was a shield from the Symbiots. Finally, there was talk that an al-Malik, Sister Theafana al-Malik, would be Empress. Duke Hakim became displeased when Alexius did not marry her, and has let his displeasure become known. A descendent of Tarif must share in the Imperial Power — to this end, he has dedicated himself.

House Culture and Ways

Yet each sad part the nobles play
While one by one the stars decay
The Hazat wars, the Hawkwood soars
And Li Halan to dogma pray
The Decados plot, while the curse
From the starless dark grows the worse
Souls are fed to the nameless dread

While al-Malik composes verse
— "The Devouring Plume," Faysul al-Malik ("The Witness of Tahir")

The Hazat Court Archivist, Phibranno, wrote "Many outsiders see House al-Malik as an isolated gang of effete, impenetrable artists, waxing gloriously obtuse about a universe they know little about. The stereotypical al-Malik *Tlassa* (cloud) glides through his life with his head in the sky and his hand in someone else's purse. As usual, the stereotype is dead wrong." Part of this prejudice comes from the secrecy the al-Malik impose on themselves and their inner beliefs, which is obscured through their daily conversations in the Graceful Tongue. This tradition was begun by Rahimat al-Malik as a way of fighting the house's decline. Elements of this tradition go back to Arif and Munir ibn Tarif. Called by Rahimat "The Way of the Three Mountains," it was a compilation of earlier beliefs. The ancients spoke of the laws of three, and even Tarif knew of the significance of the process he called "Scientific Trinitism," or Action, Reaction and Synthesis.

The Influence of Munir ibn Tarif

Tarif's Path was a way which sought the eventual salvation of the living universe. His vision has influenced various descendants, and there are those who believed he genetically tinkered with his family to produce *Asabiyah*, a family/community blessed with the powers of prophecy and insight, able to change the paths of potentiality. While many family members think this is only a myth, others, including Arif and Rahimat, stressed that Tarif's Vision was possible to experience, and had shaped the family destiny. The gifts of prophecy only come at crucial times in history, and demand that the individual surrender himself/herself to the will of Tarif. There is a minority at court that holds that Tarif's Vision includes the Way of the Three Mountains, and secretly call themselves the *Iqlim*, or "those who climb the path."

The Way of the Three Mountains

The Way of Three Mountains describes a course of enlightenment gained by successive experiences. First, one observes; then, one becomes; finally, one transcends. These three stages mark the *du shen* ("circle walk," or life-progress) of the ideal ruler, and is both a mark of distinction and a closely-guarded secret within the house. The house has stressed that these are not in conflict with the true meaning of Zebulon's teachings, but the Church hierarchy mistrusts the secrecy of the al-Malik regarding their beliefs.

As a child, a young al-Malik ascends the First Mountain by immersion in many experiences. Languages (highly valued skills within the house) are taught, as well as music, mathematics, and meditation. The child learns firsthand what is it to assume many roles, beggars, servants and members of the opposite sex, to understand how others think and feel. Their teachers (*Doy-re*, or "mind-writers") refer to young nobles as *theaa*, or "the gathering dew."

Later in the process, the young noble is sent off in disguise to learn about the galaxy and the many experiences therein. Finally saturated with experience, the noble returns to assume his/her family name. During this stage, the al-Malik searcher is known as *daya*, or "the wandering cloud."

Once the family position is assumed, the noble ascends the Second Mountain — becoming. Emerging from the family with all the noble graces and learning, the young adult al-Malik appears to an outsider as someone who has received the best education shielded away within the court. The al-Malik encourage these believes. The young noble begins to govern at this stage. Now and then the noble will slip away on a *qanat*, or secretive quest to renew their experience in the world. Assuming a disguise, they adventure again for a short sojourn, seeking experience and wisdom. Astute Doy-re may choose more promising al-Malik at this stage and teach them the sacred dances, music, codes, and laws of the universe (*Tao-do*). Many never receive this advanced training.

The Way to the Third Mountain comes when the al-Malik grows stagnant or tired with worldly rule. Discarding all possessions, the individual becomes *iha*, the mist. Removing herself to a remote spot, the al-Malik hermit becomes attuned to the higher will of the Pancreator and leaves the world possessed of experience and knowledge. Many al-Malik never make it to the third stage, becoming too emersed in governing. The uninformed think the Third Mountain is a physical place, Mount Sulh on Istakhr. But some desert mystics and seekers state that the Way of the Three Mountains cannot long thrive in a worldly court. After the third generation of teachers, unless spiritually renewed, the Way descends amidst the distractions of the court.

Tahir's Path

A few believe that Tahir's vision of the entropic demons was correct. Forbidden within the house, a few have drifted to these underground teachings. The basic tenant is that the universe is full of devouring energies, and the individual must build up *kharaj*, or a soul-tax, to feed the powers, while developing inner spiritual qualities. Eventually, through perseverance, a strengthened, purified warrior will emerge. Some antimonist cults believe Tahir to be a prophet. Al-Malik followers of Tahir's Path disdain the antimonists, stressing that Tahir was accurately reflecting reality, not embracing demonology. They emphasize that only a small aristocracy of souls can understand the implications of Tahir's Path. Little is known of it, but the following has been gleaned by other family members through difficult research and spying: Tahir warned that an individual must first build a soul through various esoteric and mental exercises while "consciously feeding" the entropic entities. Finally, through a purification process, the individual will glimpse the reality of existence. The soul builds immunities against the devouring entities as it is toughened. Only then does true "freedom" emerge. Dark powers are seen as a natural part of the universe. Tahir desired to harden and excel spiritual evolution by breaking free of the *kharaj*.

The Graceful Tongue

House legend states that the Bay'ho len Itka Tu has always existed. Its greatest expression came in the works of the 25th century poet Ban'on Be'n Kilou, whose verses, *al-Malyanna*, are considered sacred (and secret) writ. In the verses, B'en Kilou offers a collection of highly metaphorical portraits of life during the First Republic. Deciphering the meaning behind those metaphors is regarded as a sign of wisdom. Too oblique for most people to follow — let alone comprehend — they are the delight of the al-Malik Istakhr children. Arif al-Malik mastered the Graceful Tongue to confound his political enemies. His use of the term "Republic" had three meanings. The first was the obvious one, a democratically elected representative government for the Known Worlds. The second referred to a republic of all sentient beings as well as various powers of the soul over the psyche. Finally, the third, known to the ruling al-Malik, referred to the living connection of all things which is constantly present, yet little realized. Some believe the True Republic will be realized when all beings awaken to this actualization. When Rahimat al-Malik stated that the Third Republic was in all hearts, he meant that it was present but not achieved by the many. Outsiders believe the al-Malik desire a Third Republic, but the phrase contains multitudes of meaning.

The tradition of the Graceful Tongue was kept alive on Istakhr but forgotten by the house rulers during the Shaprut exile. Reintroduced by Rahimat, it produced a tendency to portray everything in terms of elaborate metaphors and images — a starship becomes the "Dust of Parvati's Eye," a sunset becomes the "Bleeding Horizon," a child becomes "the Joy and the Tear," and so on. It is considered an art form to create a variety of rich metaphors in daily speech, casting all things into an artistic and noble light. The al-Malik don't always use the Graceful Tongue, for it is an art for appropriate occasions. Yet in serious situations, such as war or diplomacy, several al-Malik members can shift into it at once, understanding each other perfectly while confounding outsiders. Al-Malik consider it a seductive language with many sensual overtones, and they disdain lovers who cannot speak eloquently. The Graceful Tongue comes into play when it is important to impress, enlighten or confuse someone else. The house's reputation for inaccessibility comes largely through skillful use of the Tongue — it's an edge they don't pass on to outsiders.

All house titles and forms of address are phrased as metaphors. Nothing means what it states at face value, and people unversed in the house language don't even understand the words, let alone the images. This frustrates suitors, spies and allies to no end; however much they might learn about House al-Malik, they will always be *ti-quen* — "Those Lost," i.e., outsiders. The speech at court is always changing style and fashion, so a provincial al-Malik, using last year's metaphors can be equally embarrassed. Prestige is displayed in al-Malik society by how familiar a speaker is with the latest changes of nuance and style in the Graceful Tongue.

All of the house can speak fluently in the regular speech of the people and the tongues of the Known Worlds (the al-Malik are masters of disguise, as are their secret police, the Mutasih). They are taught to pick up dialects readily, and the al-Malik automatically break languages down into a series of images — the root of common linguistics. Recently, there has been an artistic movement (based mainly on Aylon) away from the Graceful Tongue, called *kali-ma*. Kali-ma is plain, unadorned speech with a slight poetic bent, believed to be the expressive oral tradition of the ancient al-Malik before the Second Republic. It is seen by more rural nobles as a reaction to the artificiality of the high court. The movement is small, composed of young Aylon al-Malik and a few artisans, but as an "underground tongue," interest in it is growing.

Dress

Most al-Malik dress in brightly colored robes. A Talimanic shirt (*came-yi feth*), red with astrological symbols depicting the wearer's birthdate, is currently popular. Worn as symbolic protection during the Symbiot and Emperor Wars, they have become high court fashion. Among more rural al-Malik there is the belief that these shirts will deflect hostile intentions. Indeed, the al-Malik appear as a colorful court prepared for battle at a moment's notice. Elaborate swords and finely crafted weapons, displaying ancestry and the speaker's mottos, are common. Younger al-Malik tend to dress in simple robes of red and purple. High court women currently favor robes of dark burgundy interlaced with light blue. Outside the court there is complete freedom of dress. The Aylon al-Malik dress in an unadorned style. When Rahimat reformed the house, he instituted a strict dress code of white robes to reflect the family's humble origins, but over the years, this tradition has been neglected. On ascending to a title or rulership, it is still traditional for an al-Malik to wear a white robe.

The al-Malik are masters of disguise. Some nobles possess a "synthface" (see below), an amazing and rare device which, when placed on the face, can readily mold into convincing new facial features or be programmed with preset faces. The Mutasih possess the technology to still manufacture these wondrous devices, believed to be based on Second Republic technology, and they guard the knowledge of their creation jealously.

Advancement

An al-Malik noble traditionally advances his career by service to the court. Faithful service ensures advancement. An adventurous youth, gathering excellent information climbing the First Mountain, may be made a captain in the Mutasih. Paths of learning and information gathering are open to them, and there is little shame in entering a guild. The al-Malik have changed dynasties violently in the past, and the road to advancement in turbulent times depends largely on what faction a noble joins. There is no compulsion for a noble to join anything, but the high republican ideas of the house influence many to be of service. Critics say that they are too removed from the people they claim to speak for, yet the al-Malik hold to many republican ideals of charity and public benefits. They have a fondness for technology, displayed in their palaces and homes.

Allies and Enemies

Noble Houses

House Hawkwood: The al-Malik find the Hawkwoods necessary allies but also the least defined of the noble houses. "Scratch the Hazat, you get the army. Scratch the Li Halan, you get the Church. Scratch the Decados, you get unrestrained children. Scratch the Hawkwood, and you get the Hawkwood" was a quote attributed to Duke Hakim al-Malik. Supporting (along with the League) the claims of Alexius Hawkwood as Emperor, there is some resentment for baring the brunt against the Decados in the Emperor Wars. Still, the Hawkwoods proved reliable allies, although the al-Malik goal of destroying the Decados ended, shelved when the Decados accepted Alexius as Emperor. In the past the Hawkwoods and al-Malik have clashed over Leminkainen and Aylon.

House Decados: Their complete disregard for republican ideas marks the Decados as a more fierce opponent than even the Li Halan. For the past century al-Malik policy called for containment of the Decados power, forming alliances with other houses to keep the peace. "League trade open and the Decados contained" was long a saying among the al-Malik diplomats. Still, House al-Malik finds Decados diplomacy persuasive at times, and respects their intelligence networks. The republican ideas emanating from the al-Malik worlds have found fertile soil at times on the Decados worlds, and these ideas have done much to counter the superior spy service of the Decados.

The Hazat: Once close allies with House Chauki, House al-Malik viewed the Hazat upstarts with ferocious hatred, twice backing Chauki Pretenders on doomed crusades to retake their homeworlds. The Hazat military machine seemed invincible, so the al-Malik encouraged League boycotts and hatched plots from a distance. Finally, they accepted the inevitable — the Hazat were there to stay. Normal relations replaced earlier hatreds, but with continued suspicion on both sides. The al-Malik admired the military prowess of the Hazat, while fearing what it represented. At least one al-Malik general, following the Hazat example, tried to usurp the royal house. In the recent Emperor Wars, the two families came to blows, and the al-Malik relied on their League and spy networks to confound their mightier enemy. Attempts to spread republican/League propaganda to the Hazat military continue, with little result. "Ah, if they converted to our views, what a force we would have," Asim al-Malik said after losing to the Hazat at the Battle of Sutek.

House Li Halan: "You cannot climb the mountain while following an outdated map," said Kalila al-Malik, in reference to the Li Halan. "Perhaps after indulging the passions and then baring the chains of dogma, they will break through to the meaning of the Prophet's teachings." The two houses were friendly before the Li Halan "conversion;" afterward they became idealogical enemies. Still, the recent generation of al-Malik and Li Halan fought side by side in the Emperor Wars, and there are those who hope for amicable relations. Contention over Criticorum remains, as the Li Halan are one of many parties eyeing it.

The Church

Urth Orthodox: The Orthodox branch of the Church long feuded with the al-Malik. Often charged with not taking the Omega Gospels seriously, the al-Malik respond with quotations of their own from Zebulon's teachings. The learned al-Malik often place Orthodox debaters in verbal minefields. Few have debated theology with the al-Malik and declared victory. The Orthodoxy has none too subtly aided minor houses in rebellion against the al-Malik in the past. Yet an understanding of sorts has developed. The Church thrives on the al-Malik worlds, but in muted form. Watched over by the ruling family, it cannot publicly take stands far from al-Malik opinion. As long as the Church caters to the spiritual welfare of the people, it is fine. Both sides are suspicious of the intentions of the other. "Every Church member a republican, every al-Malik an Orthodox," an exasperated Bishop Tabari said about the goals desired by both sides.

Eskatonic Order: Generally, the al-Malik believe the Eskatonics are uncouth company, avoiding them whenever possible. There are exceptions, for as Tahir said, "There are jewels, even within cesspools." The cultivated and curious al-Malik find certain members of the Eskatonic Order fascinating, and maintain good relations with them. Along with certain Hesychasts, some Eskatonics have begun monasteries on al-Malik worlds. Two Eskatonics of note are entered into the rolls of al-Malik history: Romachka the Black, who served Tahir, and Brother Sencho, an advisor to Jabir al-Malik the Golden.

The Merchant League

Charioteers: The Charioteers and the al-Malik have been allies since the end of the Second Republic. Some Charioteers wanted to establish the Third Republic during the Emperor Wars, and were a little baffled by the al-Malik backing House Hawkwood. The reasons were explained to the more astute among them, and the al-Malik/Charioteer alliance proved useful to Alexius. Traditionally, Charioteers have had tax breaks for ports on al-Malik worlds, for which they render assistance to the family in times of war. During civil wars, the Charioteers have backed losing sides with little retribution.

Scravers: Rahimat's war was long ago. The al-Malik find this guild exceptional in uncovering Second Republic technology. Actively recruiting them for this purpose, the al-Malik have earned the nickname the "Scraver's Bank."

The Muster (Chainers): Excellent relations exist with the Chainers, which many outsiders find hypocritical of the "republican" al-Malik. The Chainers sell slaves on the Istakhr Market. They are forbidden to enslave citizens of al-Malik worlds. With the lucrative sales at the market, it would be unprofitable to do so. Several family members have invested heavily in this guild.

Aliens

Ur-Obun: Many Ur-Obun have served with honor at the al-Malik court. They have proven indispensable as advisors and diplomats, and are always welcome. Talil vornSim's friendship with Arif al-Malik and, indeed, in helping form aspects of his republican outlook, is well known throughout the al-Malik worlds.

Ur-Ukar: Since occupying Aylon, the al-Malik have treated with the Ur-Ukar through their clan leaders, playing the old game of divide and conquer. Al-Malik governors encourage inner clan rivalry, often favoring the weaker contestant until the balance of power shifts. The al-Malik, obviously, do not want a united Ur-Ukar populace seeking to regain their lost world. Still, Ur-Ukar are recruited by the al-Malik, and a company of them is found in the duke's household as soldiers (drawn from a minor clan loyal to the al-Malik). Ukarish rebellions have been violent and brutally suppressed (4780-92, 4896-92).

Holdings

Aylon

Originally colonized by the Ur-Ukar, Aylon was later conquered by a Church-lead humanity. The al-Malik later seized it from the Keddah governor, further straining relations between the two families. Surviving Ur-Ukar dwell on reservations in the northern province of Mwerrid Mokta, where they possess vast subterranean holdings. The Ur-Ukar rebelled during the Emperor Wars. This rebellion was finally crushed, and "friendly" Ur-Ukar were chosen by their conquerors to lead the clans. Zebulon the Prophet first preached on Aylon after his vision, and pilgrims annually flock to the site (known as Prophet's Hill). The northern cities of Navarre, Ryoko and Sunval are trading zones, with Sunval boasting a reputation for one of the finest casino's in the Known Worlds. Recently, interest in Ur-Ukar culture and art has increased. Mwerrid Mokta is mostly a mountainous and desert region. The southern region of Mwerrid Na'al is a temperate zone, holding vast agricultural estates and hunting reserves. Here nobles pay handsomely for the privilege of hunting the most challenging wild game animals of the Known Worlds.

The older generation of Aylon al-Malik are provincial but competent business people. Largely independent from court, they run their own affairs. The younger generation have appropriated certain Ur-Ukar ideas and survival skills. They are the house's greatest warriors. Proud, self reliant, and toughened by experience, they disdain the worldliness of the Istakhr court. Some believe that the next cycle of al-Malik rebellions will lead an Aylon al-Malik to the throne.

Criticorum

A vibrant planet with a rich economy, Criticorum's main city of Acheon is a den of plotting factions. The province of Ost holds the main ports and population centers. Refugees fleeing the Symbiot Wars have fled to the cities of Acheon, Larrane and Ostgard, overburdening the social services. Civil services have their hands full with relocation and policing. Holding Criticorum, with all its intrigues and problems, is no small task. Once a proposed site for the Second Republic capitol, Criticorum has fallen out of al-Malik hands on many occasions. Unfortunately, the Criticorum al-Malik tend to be the most decadent of the house. Pleasure seeking and remote, they enrich themselves with bribes and periodic shake downs of the transient population. Mainly centered in the southern city of Tabrast, they resent the authority of the court-appointed governor. They also claim to be the "true" al-Malik. The al-Malik governor must rely on his own spy networks and soldiery, increasing the tension between the court and local al-Malik. The southern provinces hold the great house estates and scenic areas of wondrous beauty.

Istakhr

Uninhabited when the First Republic discovered it, there were some preadamite ruins found in the region of the southern pole. Settled largely by people of mid-eastern extraction, it was the homeworld of the al-Malik and became their power center after Rahimat's Reconquest. The famous Istakhr Market in the capitol city of Samarkand is the second largest open bazaar in the Known Worlds. Here a teeming economy thrives in the vast mazes of the market. To "know the Market" is a compliment on Istakhr, for it is labyrinthine in the extreme. Great palaces, cathedrals and museums have been built from the proceeds of the Market Tax, making Samarkand "mistress of beauty." The old parliament building remains, and a parliament of representatives can be called at the duke's discretion. Old Second Republic codes survive in the Istakhr legal system, and even serfs possess the right to free legal representation. Civil codes and representation are one thing, but the noble code of the al-Malik is above common law. Only members of the house may sit in judgment of a family member.

Najran, the northern province, holds the temperate zone. Here, the city of Tioch overlooks Lake Harat. The Afid Desert, south of Samarkand, is home to wandering desert clans. The southern province of Grenada produces agriculture and holds great family estates. Native Istakhr al-Malik are the most traditional, and retain the legacies of Tarif. The more provincial branches of the family possess more family traditions and lore.

Shaprut

Home to the ungulate Shantor, the mineral wealth below the surface attracted the First Republic. The inevitable Shantor rebellion was swiftly crushed. During the Second Republic, Shaprut fell into the al-Malik purview, and the Shantor received representation. Yet with the coming of the New Dark Ages this was withdrawn as, one-by-one, republican institutions languished. The remaining Shantor dwell on reservations in the northern province of Pamott. Some suffer slave labor in the mines, an argument house enemies use against the republican ideals of the al-Malik (the sale of slaves on the Istakhr Market being the other).

The al-Malik rule from the southern city of Tabriz in Yathrid Province. Native Shaprut al-Malik are highly refined, cultivating the arts. They cultivate the singing poets of Shaprut, the *bakhshi*. Their beautiful music, recognized throughout the Known Worlds, finds inspiration on Shaprut. During the Symbiot Wars the planet suffered from raids. New garrisons on the planet disrupted the sedentary solitude once enjoyed by the people of Shaprut. Vestiges of Second Republic rule, such as the Shaprut Congress, remain. There is representation, but the congress can only be called by the Planetary Governor. Traditionally, the governor is chosen from the Shaprut al-Malik.

People

Republican ideals remain the bedrock upon which the legal codes on Shaprut and Istakhr are built. Although serfs are found on all al-Malik worlds, they can find free representation in legal cases on the above mentioned worlds. Serfs comprise roughly 70% of the al-Malik population. They are most numerous on Criticorum and Shaprut, least on Aylon. Vestiges of the middle class remain on Istakhr, centered around the Istakhr Market in Samarkand. The freemen on the al-Malik worlds (which include the vast city populations) make up about 22% of the population. Slavery is found in various forms on Shaprut, Istakhr and Criticorum, and comprises approximately 3% of the population. Again, on Istakhr and Shaprut a slave receives state legal representation free. The nobility, with its various retainers (the Church advisors, wealthy allied families, army commanders, viziers, high level administrators, diplomats, etc.) make up 5% of the population.

Aylon is the exception to the al-Malik worlds. Slavery is not practiced there, and serfs live in conditions approximating freemen, due to the low population density and rugged planet conditions. Activities unheard of on the other worlds may pass there (competent foreigners holding administrative posts, serfs running councils). A person's value is based primarily on accomplishments. Also, there is a sizable Ur-Ukar population. The young al-Malik have taken to learning from the planet's first colonizers, and a new code of values distinguishes them from the other al-Malik.

Personages

Katib Aswad Ben zahid al-Malik

Head of the Mutasih, the al-Malik secret police, Katib is well informed of activities occurring on al-Malik worlds and beyond. Forty-six years of age, he took over the organization during the Emperor Wars. He was able to lure the Hazat into some intelligence traps, but his main concern was the Decados intelligence network, the Jakovian Agency, which was always one step ahead of him. Beyond bribery, he replaced some of the older Mutasih intelligence officers with a younger set. To his embarrassment, the vizier was found to be in Decados pay, discovered by a young noble with no diplomatic or spy service. A bigger disappointment was to follow.

To Katib's regret, he discovered his second-in-command, his lifelong friend and half-brother, Rashad, was also in the service of the Decados. The evidence was irrefutable, something he stumbled on himself. No one else knew. He could turn Rashad over, but a mistake this large would dishonor both him and his family. Finally, he knew what he had to do. He called on Rashad, telling him that the duke was to meet them in the Istakhr Market at night, to pass on sensitive information concerning the Emperor. The two went forth in disguise, joking as was their way. In the midst of the labyrinthine market, near the perfume bazaar, Katib pulled out a ceremonial dagger and stabbed his lieutenant repeatedly through the heart, and then stole his money. The next day he appeared shocked when the body of his half-brother was found, dead in the Market and robbed of his goods by a desperate thief. Katib told no one of what really happened, and his half-brother's reputation was intact. Still, the slaying of Rashad haunts Katib. He is prone to melancholy bouts. A serious man, he now looks far older than his years. He has found that his best agents tend to be from Aylon, and now recruits heavily from that planet.

Safa al-Malik

Born on Aylon, Safa traveled to Criticorum and Byzantium Secundus during her Way to the First Mountain. She was disgusted at how decadent the Criticorum al-Malik had become. Returning to Aylon, she immersed herself in the teachings of an Ur-Ukar shaman, learning survival skills and wisdom. During the Emperor Wars, Safa volunteered for a military assignment and distinguished herself against the Decados and Hazat in battle. Retiring

after the wars with the title of captain, Safa took up her duties on the family estate.

Tiring of her duties, she went the Way of the Second Mountain, first living among the Ur-Ukar and then fighting briefly against the Symbiots. Lately, she has taken up with a group of Scravers, combing the Known Worlds for old Second Republic technology. Safa's kin on Aylon tell her they are tired of the current regime, and this gives her pause, for she had a curious vision among the Ur-Ukar, one on which Duke Hakim was dead and she approached the throne. She has not spoken to anyone about this.

Twenty-seven and dark haired, Safa is a skilled duelist, poet and warrior. Honest but short tempered, she little resembles the image most have of the al-Malik — something she is well aware of.

Roleplaying
Al-Malik Characters

Players may create many types of al-Malik characters for roleplaying. Ideas include:

- A mystic noble poet, unconcerned with worldly matters (think of notable Sufi teachers or the poet Rumi).
- A practical republican, one of the al-Malik who looks to government and gradual change to rectify the social ills of the Known Worlds.
- A member of the secret police, the Mutasih, spying on transactions in the Istakhr Market.
- A decadent al-Malik baron from Criticorum, unconcerned with anything save his own pleasure, a heavy gambler (e.g., the Egyptian king Farouk)
- A wealthy collector of obscure Second Republic technology, willing to pay handsomely for rare items.
- A proud lesser member of the Shaprut line, claiming the real descent and plotting to overturn the house.
- A duchess claiming descent from Tahir the Doomed and a follower of his path.
- A noble scholar, possessing vast heretical and historical works about the past.
- An explorer, traveling with the Charioteers.
- An Aylon al-Malik, knowledgeable about Ur-Ukar lore and a good warrior.

Gamemastering al-Malik

Dramas centering around the al-Malik can occur anywhere in the Known Worlds, since their wealth is vast. They tend to be explorers, and travel the Known Worlds during their youth (usually under an assumed name).

The al-Malik homeworlds provide a fertile ground for campaigns. Criticorum is crawling with competing spy networks (Imperial, Li Halan, Decados, League, Ukar, Church, and al-Malik). Many factions covet the rich planet, and some of the native al-Malik dream of seizing power; they find many friendly ears for their endeavors. Since the planet has a vibrant economy, the court doesn't want it to slip away. Player characters can get involved with any faction.

The vast Istakhr Market, stretching through a third of the city of Samarkand, provides innumerable opportunities for adventure. Perhaps a Charioteer is giving information to an Imperial spy. The al-Malik secret police, the Mutasih, and the Decados also need the information. Since the marketplace is labyrinthine, the player characters (working for one of the factions) must navigate the outdoor market, avoiding enemies, thieves and pitfalls, to deliver or intercept the information. Other adventures in the Marketplace can include:

- An important Hazat heir has been caught by the Chainers, but has not revealed his/her identity. Going on sale in the slave bazaar, the players must rescue the heir before anti-Hazat forces realize who the Chainers have (this could include different factions of the al-Malik court).
- The Scravers have placed some "harmless" Preadamite sculpture on sale. The sculpture contains a deadly virus, the same which caused the Bone Plague of 4101. The players, tipped by some early "contained" plague victims, follow the trail to the Scravers Bazaar to prevent the sale and quarantine the deadly virus. Again, various agents want the viral infected sculpture for germ warfare.
- The anarchist poet, ibn Sorhab ibn Musa, is distributing anti-al-Malik propaganda somewhere in the marketplace. The Mutasih are closing in, but a rich Li Halan noble wants him whisked off planet (any anti-republican propaganda is good propaganda for the Li Halan). The player characters are hired by one of the factions.

Traits
Learned Skill
Language (Graceful Tongue)

All al-Malik know the Graceful Tongue to some degree (learning at least one level in the skill). Those from Shaprut and Istakhr are masters of it, while the Criticorum al-Malik use it in a somewhat older style (the court style of 50 years ago). The older Aylon al-Malik use it sparingly and the young disdain it for more plain, unsubtle speech. Aylon al-Malik are proud of their "differences" from most of the family, and see themselves as more virtuous then their other cousins. Some believe that they will run the house one day. Already the best military commanders and fighters are from Aylon.

When speaking the Graceful Tongue, a character speaks in metaphors. Whether these are understood depends on how well the listener knows the Graceful Tongue, for it is a language steeped in cultural, historical and mythologicial references. Usually, a roll is only required for difficult or deliberately obtuse statements. Characters who do not know the Tongue may be allowed occasional Wits + Lore (al-Malik) to get the jist of certain statements.

Affliction

Dark Glimpse (1 pts): During his training in the Way of the Three Mountains, the character saw a prophetic vision of universal or personal doom, or misinterpreted a vision. The character may not want to share this vision, but it shapes his behavior. Recovering from a Dark Glimpse is brought about by experience or deep reflection. Sometimes asking about the meaning to those experienced in such things helps, as does incorporating it into a wider philosophy (such as Tahir's Path). While the character may be able to hide his morbid outlook most of the time, it will show through to those who know him, and occasionally strangers will also notice. Over time, the character may get a reputation as unbalanced or even be considered the pawn of darker powers by some.

Equipment

Synthface

This ultrathin, adhesive variant of synthflesh was first engineered by Second Republic medical technicians, and used to reconstruct severely damaged facial muscles and skin. Bonding to DNA chemical information upon contact, it takes on the shape and hue of the surrounding features, and can be molded to cover over damaged areas. The chameleon quality of a synthface was first noticed by the al-Malik, who poured money into secret research, eventually developing a model perfect for intelligence gathering: a spy mask. Using nanotech computers woven into the chemically-sensitive synthetic flesh, this model could take upon different features than the wearer's own — even storing a number of preprogrammed facial features. With the addition of organic dyes to change coloration, the al-Malik spies could change their color and shape.

The common synthface is rare enough, found among the Amaltheans but among few others (some wealthy patrons seek them out to hide wartime disfigurations). A spy synthface, however, is an al-Malik secret, manufactured after the Fall only by their technicians. Some of the devices have, of course, spread to other factions, but the manufacturing secret has yet to be decoded by others.

The raw form of a synthface is a thin, featureless, circular layer of synthetic skin. It is wrapped around the user's face and held tight for 30 seconds while it molds to the user's face (the user must hold his breath during this time). If preprogrammed faces are available, they can be activated during this formation period by certain facial expressions — a frown accompanying a smile may trigger the "Count Eustas" program, whereby the synthface forms into the shape of Count Eustas's well-known mug. Each programmed "face" will have its own expression triggers. Once formed, the face is a perfectly real and can pass all inspections. However, this lasts for only about 24 hours before it must be renewed. Once the time limit is up, if the synthface has not been removed, the character will be literally faceless. If the face stays on for another 24 hours, the user will begin to suffocate as the air passages close up.

The synthface is removed with the application of a chemical solvent (Colloid -12), which causes the device to slide from the user's face, assuming its featureless form. The face cannot be used again for one hour, after which it can be used as normal. For this reason, spies on long-term missions usually carry two synthfaces, lest they be caught without their face at an embarrassing moment.

It is an extremely expensive and time-consuming process to manufacture a synthface. For this reason, most current 'faces are artifacts handed down along family lines. However, age and use does affect a synthface, with older or over-used models developing flaws — sometimes working perfectly at first, but then "melting" before onlookers' eyes. (Give these old models a number to roll under on a d20 not to malfunction.)

Programming a particular face requires a massive amount of data. Usually, the target's face must be photographed from all angles by a special video camera. The info is then fed into the synthface's nanonet, which calculates the final face. Often, multiple tries must be made before the face is just right. Some synthfaces may be given to spies with flaws unnoticed by their programmers, who may never have seen the targets' faces themselves, only video images of them.

While a synthface may simulate a person's features, it does not affect voice or behavior. For this reason, the skills Acting and Disguise may prove necessary for a spy.

Costs:

TL 7: A common synthface for the medical reconstruction of the natural face (or other skin) costs 3000 firebirds. This type of device cannot assume other faces, only the face of its wearer. It is mainly used to cover scars or other disfigurements. The Colloid-12 solvent used to remove it costs 1 firebird per use.

TL 8: This spy model includes the nanotech computers necessary for assuming alter-egos. Cost is 10,000 firebirds (or 7 Benefice pts) plus 3,000 (or 2 Benefice pts) per programmed face. In addition, it costs 1000 (or 1 Benefice pt) per face which can be held in memory (to a maximum of five). Thus, a synthface which can assume the features of only one target would cost 14,000 firebirds (or 10 Benefice pts) if it comes with that target pre-programmed in. Subtract five points from the Benefice cost for a malfunctioning model (only works on a d20 roll of 13 or less).

Yearning to Rise: Minor Houses

by Nicky Rea and Sam Chupp

Juandaastas

(wahn-DAH-stus)

The stares began when they were announced at the al-Malik's reception. Not-quite-audible comments and stifled laughter followed their circuit of the room. Though self-discipline prevented Alinia HanSaval-Juandaastas from sighing in exasperation, she dreaded these affairs. Leonald Juandaastas and she had been married a scant three months, but were already the hot item discussed by every bored noble from here to Byzantium Secundus. The novelty of an Ur-Obun-human marriage had not yet worn thin. Sometimes she wondered how they had missed all the prior Ur-Obun marriages into the Juandaastas line. Dreading a repeat of the last party, she recalled the slurs and hostility, praying that this time Leonald would have no need of his fancy dress sword to defend her honor.

Advocates of equal rights for aliens, patrons of alien arts, the Juandaastas occupy a unique position among the noble houses. Several members of this pioneering family have married Ur-Obun. They sponsor Vorox dance and martial arts exhibitions and other cultural events to promote understanding and appreciation of aliens among the Church, guilds and nobility. Particularly concerned that the spiritual qualities alien groups bring to their interactions with humanity shine through, the Juandaastas deplore the results of terraforming and are disgusted by the alien reservation system. While they have long-standing ties to both the Ur-Obun and the Vorox, many members of the house seek out unexplored territory, looking for new sentient races. They lead the diplomatic negotiations with the Oro'ym of Madoc, a recently rediscovered sentient race long thought extinct.

Among members of House Juandaastas, the high incidence of psychic and theurgic ability coupled with their uncanny self-control can be traced back to the Second

Republic, when Ur-Obun-human unions were capable of producing offspring (through genetic manipulation). Now, though marriages between the two continue, it is no longer possible for them to produce children — except in the rarest case in which a Juandaastas happens to carry the exact genes necessary to link with her Ur-Obun spouse. Because of this childless state, the Juandaastas introduced the practice of taking noble concubines (to bear or father a child for the couple, who would then raise it as their own). Concubines are treated as sister-wives or brother-husbands among the Juandaastas; their advice and counsel is welcomed, their children know them as their biological parents, and they are accorded both status and respect. Among other noble houses, this is not always the case.

History of the House

Juandaastas has always held a minor place along the fringes of the noble houses. Rather than scheming to better their own position and take their place among the major noble houses, however, they chose to lobby for alien rights and reach out to other sentients — an understandable reaction if the house's rumored origins are true. Popular belief attributes the formation of House Juandaastas to the consolidation of numerous groups who had long sought sentient life among the stars. Intermarriage over several generations created House Juandaastas.

Almost from the beginning of human contact with alien races, the leaders of the house urged that understanding and compassion rule all dealings with other sentients — or so they claim. Their detractors say that the house's support for alien rights came only after its multiple attempts to rise to major house status failed. Having nothing to lose, it sought a new path to power. House members counter that its failure to rise came as a result of Juandaastas' open support for aliens. Whichever came first,

they were unable to prevent the wholesale terraforming of many planets and the ills visited upon sentient races like the Shantor. Their sincerity, however, garnered the attention of the Ur-Obun, resulting in several marriages between the spiritual aliens and House Juandaastas.

During the heyday of the Second Republic, scientists discovered a way to combine Ur-Obun and human genes, making it possible for fertilization to occur and children to be born, though most such were test tube babies. Ur-Obun genes were thus cross-bred into the Juandaastas line. Sadly, the secret of such genetic mixing was lost with the Fall. For a time, those of House Juandaastas were placed under the intense scrutiny of the Church, who equated them with the genetically engineered. The house played almost no role in the Emperor Wars, though it supported Hawkwood because of that house's protection of the Ur-Obun. It is currently engaged in the search for other sentient beings and in secretly trying to rediscover the genetic engineering that allowed the two races to bear children.

House Culture and Ways

As might be expected, the Juandaastas are usually well-developed spiritually, both through their open-minded stance regarding aliens and through their direct association with the Ur-Obun. The Juandaastas tend toward philosophy and diplomacy. This is not to say they have no warriors among them; many Juandaastas are renowned for their knowledge of tactics and understanding of alien thought. One such, Rainart Juandaastas, serves as a consultant regarding the threat posed by the Symbiots, while Tereseann Juandaastas serves as an ambassador to the Vau.

Leaders of the house expect family members to support their aims, keeping family secrets such as the family's high incidence of psychic ability and its genetic research from discovery by the Church. House members who join the clergy tend toward the Preceptors, the Eskatonic Order or the Amaltheans. Even then, they are encouraged to keep the interests of their house in mind. Because House Juandaastas is engaged in secret and forbidden research, its members like to appear unassuming and non-threatening. Their clothing, armor and weapons are well-made; these items, their hairstyles and personal adornment follow fashion closely enough that members of the house blend in — the best policy for hiding what they are up to. Aside from protecting family interests, most Juandaastas have a reputation for kindness, compassion and the bravery to stand up for their beliefs.

Younger members who marry Ur-Obun, sponsor cultural events, serve as diplomats and advance the fortunes of the house are often accorded rank and given estates to manage. Though not large, such estates can be found on several pleasant planets, most often on those held by either House Hawkwood or House al-Malik. Their support of and ties to the Engineers is the house's most closely-guarded secret. While they distrust Orthodox clergy, and by extension, the Li Halan, they save their disgust for the Avestites.

Holdings

The main Juandaastas holdings are on Criticorum, where they manage three al-Malik estates that abut their own. Aside from overseeing the fruit orchards which comprise the majority of the properties, they frequently serve diplomatic functions keeping, the various travelers who use the world's many jumproads happy and preventing war from breaking out among them. They own forestry concerns granted them by the Hawkwoods on Gwynneth, occupy a small estate and maintain part of the bazaar on Istakhr, and have manor houses on the other Hawkwood and al-Malik worlds. More recently, they have acquired the rights to one of the floating islands of Madoc, where they plan to build the labs necessary for their genetic research project. In return, they gave the Engineers their old skimmer factory and all rights to production of the Juandaastas Slider.

Personnel

House Juandaastas generally treats its serfs well, refuses to deal in slave labor, and employs trusted soldiers as its house guard. Serfs who show promise are occasionally offered the chance to join the guard. Younger Juandaastas often learn military command skills by spending a year or two commanding the house guard. Only a few members of the house can afford technology more advanced than a personal shield. While their guards are well armed (bearing swords, crossbows and, where needed, guns), they mostly wear leather armor. Juandaastas doesn't keep its holdings through force, but through virtue of having powerful friends (Hawkwood and al-Malik). Further, as many members of the family are psychic, they are rarely caught unawares.

Leading Juandaastas: Marquessa Sabine al-Malik-Juandaastas (widow of the former head of the household who assumed that role upon his death), Baron Kaspar Juandaastas (the heir apparent, currently serving as advisor on alien affairs to Emperor Alexius).

Typical Juandaastas Traits
Characteristics: Alien, Faith
Natural skills: Observe
Learned skills: Focus, Lore (Ur-Obun), Read Obunish (or other alien writing), Social (Debate), Speak Obunish (or other alien tongue), Xeno-Empathy
Blessings/Curses: Strong-Willed (2 pts: +2 Stoic Mind when resisting others' or own psychic Urge)/ Outraged (+2 pts: -2 Calm when discussing alien rights)
Benefices: Alien Contacts, Major House Patronage

Justinian
(just-IN-ee-in)

"Loyalty Unto Death! As if they really understood what that means. Look what they're forcing you into!" Carolandra Justinian fumed to her younger sister Juliette. The smaller woman, resplendent in the gown she would wear when she married Evan Hawkwood next week, shook her head and laughed, "Really, 'Landra, how can you object to this? I'm joining the Imperial family!"

Carolandra stood. Walking to the door, she turned and shrugged, "You're being sold like a slave. But then, I don't suppose you mind. After all, you're getting an Imperial husband. Whatever happened to our pride?"

Justinian is a house divided against itself. Once a major house, staunch supporters of Vladimir, its fortunes plummeted in the wake of his assassination. After centuries of near-obscurity, the house is currently trying to rebuild the family fortunes and gain back lost holdings. Its members desperately seek alliances with other nobles, especially the royal houses. Their preferred method of gaining allies is to marry daughters of the house to suitable prospects, a strategy that has enraged some younger members —especially Dame Carolandra Justinian, whose exploits as a knight rival those of her kinswoman, Dame Octavia.

The house motto, "Loyalty Unto Death," is interpreted quite differently depending on which Justinian faction each member belongs to. The Old Guard consists of most of the house leaders. Its policy is to decide which major houses to ally with, seal those alliances with marriage, and use those contacts to regain lost holdings and make House Justinian great once again.

Several younger members, led in open revolt by Dame Carolandra, angrily repudiate their elders' schemes, claiming that marriage alliances merely send sons and daughters of the family away to strengthen other houses. They advocate taking male or female concubines, requiring them to swear allegiance to Justinian and raise a new generation of sons and daughters to carry on the family name. They insist that once enough Justinians exist to take their holdings back, the house will regain its status.

Carolandra and her cohorts act as soldiers-of-fortune, lawgivers and advisors in various fields, seeking allies through work and comradeship. While they have not yet actually come into physical conflict with their own house members, some feel it is only a matter of time until they do. Neither side truly wants that, as there is still genuine feeling among family members regardless of whom they support. Carolandra's philosophy of total self-denial in pursuit of rebuilding the house's fortunes has been embraced as a sort of holy credo by most of her followers.

History of the House

Claiming to trace its line back to some of the original immigrants to space, House Justinian first established itself during the Diaspora, claiming a planet called Paradise and its three moons as its holdings. The tropical climes prevalent on the planet and moons allowed the family to supply many other worlds with succulent fruits, fish and exotic medicinal plants. Blessed also with mineral wealth, the Justinian holdings made it one of the richest and most influential major houses.

Justinian knights distinguished themselves in both the Ukar War and Vladimir's campaigns against the barbarians. One of the leading 10 houses at the time, House Justinian was awarded scepters, signifying its right as electors to vote on Vladimir's successor. In return, the Justinians pledged their eternal alliance to House Alecto, an honorable oath that would cost them their status, their holdings, and almost finish them as a house.

When Vladimir was assassinated at his coronation, his war-ravaged house fell to minor status. Having lost many sons itself, Justinian nevertheless kept its pledge, attempting to protect House Alecto from those who would steal its holdings and assassinate its people. Expending most of its remaining manpower, Justinian was not able to prevent the extinction of House Alecto. Though it inherited a few of Alecto's minor holdings, its own planet became a Lost World, made inaccessible through the forced closure of its jumpgate.

No one knows who tampered with the jumpgate or even how it was done (though many hint that the Decados were behind the deed), but somehow it became scrambled and no longer matched its coordinates. Having lost the world which provided the house with most of its revenue and half its family — and thus its claim to major house status — the new leader of House Justinian pulled his troops out of battle and began consolidating what the family still had. The house traded its scepters of electorship to the Orthodox Church in return for the Church's support of its continuation as a noble house. With Church protection, House Justinian has hung on to a few holdings.

Simply maintaining its reduced status has proved a considerable challenge up to the present time. Its allies acknowledge Marquis Argus Justinian as the rightful leader of the house. Still, it took Dame Octavia Justinian's, among others, unswerving efforts to retain the house's few remaining holdings, fighting off all those who would lay claim to them.

The primary business of the house is to regain its lost glory. Most have given up ever again seeing their homeworld or the rest of their family. Others believe that someday the jumpgate to Paradise will reopen and House Justinian will be whole once again.

House Culture and Ways

Loyalty and honor are very important to members of House Justinian. Even its enemies agree that its members have always kept their sworn word and supported those with whom they ally. Younger members, in particular, seem consumed with righteous fervor and the desire to prove themselves. All members of the house appear to be ravenously ambitious, the result of their relatively small numbers and desire to reclaim their proud heritage. The only thing they defend more arduously than their side of the argument is each other. They may fight amongst themselves, but let an outsider threaten any Justinian and the whole clan bonds together to eliminate the threat.

Most of the Old Guard prefer conservative dress that reflects their noble status. The younger members who have joined Carolandra's faction prefer more modern dress or quasi-military attire. When in battle, most Justinians (Old Guard or Young Turks) wear studded leather armor. Some few have inherited old ceramsteel armor that actually fits.

Whereas merit once determined who rose to higher rank within the house, now the Old Guard promotes those who support its policies, obeys its leadership and agrees to advantageous marriages. Carolandra's followers, denied advancement within the structure of the house, have assigned themselves rank. Carolandra herself refuses to acknowledge the current minor status of her house, claiming the title "princess" rather than "marquessa."

Traditional allies of House Justinian include House Hawkwood, House Li Halan and House Torenson. It considers the Decados to be enemies and suspects the Hazat of wanting to take over its holdings. Justinian staunchly support the Orthodoxy in return for its protection and has minor ties to the Charioteers.

Holdings

Justinian holdings now consist of two major manors and farmlands on Midian and minor manors controlling valuable mining concerns on Delphi. House members oversee the quality of workmanship produced by the craftsmen of Tethys for the Emperor.

Personnel

Justinian's serfs are treated fairly, if somewhat distantly. Most are farm workers or miners. Because there are so few Justinians left, the house hires mercenaries as guards. While it tries to screen those it hires, it knows some spies may be introduced into the house in this fashion. A special crack unit is made up of young members who support the Old Guard. These dedicated soldiers are known as the Silent Guard.

Leading Justinians: Marquis Argus Justinian (acknowledged head of the household and father of Carolandra), "Princess" Carolandra Justinian (head of the rebel faction), Baroness Phaedra Justinian (head of quality control on Tethys).

Typical Justinian Traits
Characteristics: Dexterity, Passion, Extrovert
Natural skills: Impress, Melee
Learned skills: Fencing Actions, Etiquette, Social (Leadership),
Blessings/Curses: Loyal (2 pts: +2 Passion when aiding sworn ally)/ Stubborn (+1 pt: -1 Calm when forced to change plans)
Benefices: Church contacts, Inheritance (ceramsteel armor)

Keddah
(ked-DAW)

Hisham Keddah pulled his cowl more closely around his face, hoping anyone who might be interested would see nothing more than a mendicant monk resting from his journeys. He wondered, not for the first time, if exchanging the overlordship of the demonic Decados for that of the heretical al-Malik was really much of an improvement. He would wait five more minutes for his contact to show, but the Decados spy trailing him was too close to risk staying any longer.

The only minor house to retain control of its own planet, House Keddah of Grail once boasted the status of a major house. Victims of a convoluted series of secondary alliances, it finds itself unwillingly bound to the Decados and at war with the al-Malik. The people of Grail consider House Keddah to be their liege lords beyond the claims of the Royal Houses or even the Emperor.

Blessed with a planet rich with vast forests of hardwoods and mountains with granite, marble, and a rare metal known as Keddite, House Keddah has managed to remain rich despite its diminished status. It once possessed the planet Aylon, but have long since lost it to the al-Malik.

Though House Keddah has always before honored its pledges, it now find itself in the position of attempting to rid itself of its forced alliance with the Decados while petitioning the al-Malik for their aid in doing so. Many members of the house have had to become covert operatives. Even when supposedly unsuited to the position, many find themselves excelling at it.

History of the House

House Keddah traces its origins to several important middle eastern families — among them, the Altari, cousins to House Hamid (who once ruled Byzantium Secundus). In honor of the tribes from which they sprang, Keddah nobles used to insist that their house leader be referred to as "sheik". Though they still do so within the family and ask their serfs and crafters to do likewise, they no longer have the power to insist on anything. Keddah's historians say that members of the house helped lead some of the original colonists through the jumpgate to Sutek.

When Keddah claimed the planet of Grail (not its

original name) during the Diaspora, the original inhabitants, a sentient avian race called the Etyri, offered to share the world with their "wingless visitors." Though the humans did not initially understand the Etyri, non-threatening gestures made by both sides eased tensions and House Keddah took possession of the "unwanted homes" (at ground level).

Relations became very strained when the Etyri realized that House Keddah intended to harvest their trees and delve into their mountains. Diplomacy failed to resolve the issue and warfare between the two races broke out. Intervention from House Juandaastas allowed the two sides to reach an accord, but not before many Etyri and humans were slain. Nonetheless, though the Etyri reside only on Grail, they are not confined to a restricted reservation, but roam freely across the planet.

Meanwhile, the family's fortunes seemed to be on the rise when it acquired Shaprut from House Torenson in exchange for a pledge of fealty should Torenson go to war with al-Malik (whose ancestors had been traditional rivals of Keddah). When Torenson was forced to pledge fealty to House Dextrite, which was then taken over by House Masseri, Keddah was forced to honor its ancient pledge to Torenson through aiding Masseri in its war against al-Malik. By then, shifting fortunes had made Keddah a minor house. The Decados conquered a weakened House Masseri and have prolonged the war between Masseri (now bound to Decados through conquest) and al-Malik, thus keeping House Keddah in its thrall as well. The planet of Shaprut had long since been claimed by al-Malik.

In recent times, secret emissaries from Keddah have contacted House al-Malik, suggesting that the Royal House assist them in divesting themselves of their hated pledge to Masseri, and through them to the Decados. Negotiations are proceeding, though many housemembers think al-Malik is asking too much in return. Further complicating the matter, the Hazat has made a feint toward taking Grail from the Keddah after its thinly-veiled attempt to take over via subsuming Keddah into its own ranks failed. Diplomats from the house frantically seek the Emperor's censure against the Hazat, knowing the house cannot stand against that warlike house's military forces.

House Culture and Ways

House Keddah has always pointed with pride to its reputation for honoring its word — even when doing so has been detrimental to its best interests. In truth, however, Keddah has never had any real choice. The family expects its members to act with honor toward all honorable foes, which does not include people like the Decados, whom they despise. Against the Decados, anything goes — spying, sabotage, lies, setting them up, and any other sort of underhanded dealing the house can get away with. Naturally, some members of the house are more willing than others to behave in this fashion. A more conservative element within the house feels that such things lower them to the level of the Decados. The two sides coexist by a simple expedient: Keddah saboteurs don't tell the conservatives what they're doing and the conservatives agree not to ask them.

Those of House Keddah wear fashionable, though not ostentatious clothing. Conservatives feel that house members should dress appropriately, while saboteurs use fashion as protective coloration. Rank within the house is awarded by merit. Members who serve the interests of the house (covert or otherwise) and distinguish themselves do not go unrewarded.

Though it has been at odds with the al-Malik for almost a century, House Keddah is now secretly allied with them — at least in theory. While the al-Malik are willing to help Keddah escape the Decados, they want Keddah's pledge to them and a portion of their resources in return. While negotiations continue, the alliance is not yet an actuality. Masseri, conquered victims of Decados scheming, are nominal allies of House Keddah. Sadly, though both houses suffer similarly, there is little trust between them. Because of the Hazat's recent actions, many of House Keddah consider them the greatest threat to their fortunes and continued existence as a separate house.

Keddah has a firm alliance with the Church. Grail is known as the planet on which Amalthea healed the Prophet and a Sanctuary Aeon monastery was established there. Because Keddah graciously granted the monastery some lands and revenues and supports its work, Keddah benefits from its healing abilities. Keddah's serfs and personnel are some of the healthiest anywhere.

Holdings

Grail is the only planet held by the Keddah. Hardwoods from their vast forests, especially the beautiful red-gold Baryana, are much prized on Kish, Pyre, Cadavus and other planets whose wood resources are severely limited. Blue veined marble from the Etyriani Mountains is sold throughout the Known Worlds, and even appreciated by the barbarians of the Kurga Caliphate. Keddite, a rare metal, was once used extensively in Second Republic manufacturing, but is now used to make adornments.

Personnel

Aside from the farmworkers, most Keddah serfs are loggers and miners. Those who show real flair are promoted to stonecutting, jewelry-making and furniture crafting. Now considered freemen, they are elevated to the status of craftsmen and trained by hired guildmembers. Keddah's soldiers and house guard consist of both hereditary and newly-promoted serf levies. Proud of their martial skills and higher status, most Keddah forces are extremely loyal and conscientious.

Leading Keddah: Sheik (Marquis) Haroun Keddah (head of the family), Deacon Sahar of Grail (healer at Sanc-

tuary Aeon monastery on Grail), Ra'ida Keddah (guild liaison on Grail), General Coman Keddah (head of the Keddah army).

Typical Keddah Traits
Characteristics: Wits, Perception
Natural skills: Dodge, Observe, Shoot, Sneak
Learned skills: Etiquette, Inquiry, Knavery
Blessings/Curses: Alert (2 pts: +2 Perception to spy on rivals)/ Untrustworthy (+1 pt: -1 Knavery).
Benefices: Secrets

Masseri

(mazz-er-EYE)

Yordana drew her gun and fired, sliding to a prone position to give the reavers as little target area as possible. She'd known when she took on this job that it would be particularly dangerous. Why else would they have hired mercenaries?

Though never one of the major houses, Masseri was formerly one of the strongest among the minor nobility. Once the overlords of Daishan, House Masseri lost almost everything when its planet became infested by the Symbiots. Conquered by the Decados, Masseri is inextricably locked into an ongoing war with al-Malik. With their holdings almost nonexistent, and the family forced into token support for the Decados, most younger members have given up on the continuation of their house and sought elsewhere for their fortunes. Many of House Masseri have renounced their house and noble status altogether, becoming adventurers and mercenaries or joining Church or guild. They have no idea what the head of their family plans.

Embittered by the imminent demise of his family line, determined to exact vengeance from the Decados, Marquis Claudio Masseri plans to open a door to disaster that the Known Worlds may not be capable of closing again. Under the guise of recovering family treasures, abandoned when they fled the Symbiots, Claudio has hired a freelance cargo pilot to take him to Daishan. Having assured the pilot that there is no longer any danger (after all, there are currently soldiers and Brother Battle monks in residence on the planet), he plans to gather up dormant seeds of the Symbiots, transport them to all the Decados worlds and free them to wreak havoc. Feeling that his own family is dead already, he cares little what happens to anyone else anymore.

History of the House

Those who eventually formed House Masseri were once a small community of religious dissenters, devoted followers of Sathraism who made several jumps away from the more established planets in order to continue practicing their faith after it was outlawed by the First Republic. Concerned with building its new society, the house failed (for a time) to notice the disappearance of most of

its pilots as they jumped to further points and didn't return. Eventually, however, the practice of jumping to more distant worlds was curtailed and cautious contact was once again established with the Known Worlds.

With the loss of most of their pilots, the Masseri — like the First Republic masters they had fled from — installed buffers to prevent the Sathraic visions from affecting their people. Even without the visions, they held to their religion for about a century after most others had forgotten it. They rejoined the Known Worlds and soon were conducting brisk trade, offering their rich grain, exotic spices and plentiful daivaka oil fuel in return for manufactured items. As the sovereign power on their planet, they sought and were granted noble status.

They hoped to become a major house when they subsumed the weakening House Dextrite, allying themselves first through marriage, then taking over all their holdings and "adopting" the Dextrites into House Masseri. In retaliation for this affront to its allies, House al-Malik declared war on Masseri. The Masseri forced House Keddah of Grail to support them in their war against the al-Malik in honor of an almost forgotten pledge to House Torenson, who were in turn bound by treaty to Dextrite. Despite (or because of) the convoluted nature of these alliances, Masseri could never quite put together a decisive victory. Weakened almost to the point of collapse, Masseri proved an easy target for a Decados takeover. Though left in charge of Daishan, House Masseri was now in thrall to Decados demands.

Then the Symbiots descended on their planet, infesting everything. The Masseri were forced to flee their fiefs. At first, no one would grant the fleeing family sanctuary, terrified of infestation themselves. Finally, a small deviant religious community with early ties to Sathraism allowed the Masseri to land on icy Cadavus and took them in. From there, they have rebuilt as best as they can. The family now trades in furs, and is required to give one tenth of its profit to the Decados.

House Culture and Ways

Ostensibly still at war with the al-Malik and under the thumb of Decados, House Masseri is a ghost of its former self. Most do not even trouble to wear the house badge any more. While Marquis Claudio Masseri proudly and stubbornly maintains his diminished court from his manor on Cadavus, most of the younger family members have fled to other planets seeking new lives. Perhaps because of their Sathraic origins, many from House Masseri have a mystical bent.

The accepted method of gaining rank within the house is to follow the marquis' orders and give verbal support to his stated plans (which do not include the scheme to infest the Decados planets; that is his secret alone). Quite simple and straightforward. Those who disagree either leave or resign themselves to a life of low rank. Because they have no holdings, their rank means little to other houses. A Masseri baron may be seated below a mere knight from one of the landed houses. (The Rank Benefice for Masseri nobles costs one point less than usual.)

Officially, House Masseri supports the Decados and is "allied" with House Keddah. It is in a declared war with House al-Malik. In actuality, Keddah and Masseri ignore one another as much as possible, each mistrusting the other. Masseri is a subject house of the Decados, having almost given up hope of eventual freedom. The war with the al-Malik has degenerated into slurs and name-calling at social functions and the occasional hostile missive sent back and forth. The al-Malik could wipe out Masseri in a heartbeat were they not afraid Decados would use such an action as an excuse to invade al-Malik territories. Those who have left their family have foresworn all household alliances and feuds, declaring themselves independent of any former ties. They have no friends or enemies they do not make for themselves. While their house is little respected, the demands placed upon the Masseri by their harsh existence (compared to most nobles) have made them a tough, hardy family.

Holdings

While they are allowed to oversee a couple of the less valuable Decados holdings on Severus, House Masseri's one claim to land is on snow-covered Cadavus, where the marquis maintains his court. More a fur trapping and trading outpost than noble court, Mansion Masseri is one of the poorest holdings occupied by a minor house. That Masseri's days are numbered, no one doubts.

Personnel

Masseri has few serfs, most of whom are engaged in fur-trapping. Because their jobs take them away from the holding for long periods of time, Masseri's serfs are more like freemen — independent and self-sufficient. Were they not branded with the Masseri symbol, they could escape elsewhere and become independent operators. Most do not attempt it only because they fear Decados will hunt them down to prevent the loss of their percentage. A minor functionary of the Decados oversees the fur business and some Decados families train their guards by assigning them first to a year's service with the Masseri.

Leading Masseri: Marquis Claudio Masseri (dictatorial head of the family), Lina Masseri (renowned mercenary and swordswoman).

Typical Masseri Traits

Characteristics: Body characteristics
Natural skills: Fight, Shoot, Vigor
Learned skills: Remedy, Ride, Survival, Warfare (Military Tactics)
Blessings/Curses: Hardy (1 pt: +1 Vigor to resist fatigue)/ Bitter (+2 pts: -2 Calm when dealing with other noble houses)
Benefices: Disenfranchised Rank (Rank costs -1 point less than usual), Well-Traveled

Shelit
(shell-IT)

Dyn-1 bent over the baron's arm, tsking quietly to himself. The Shelit looked up at the higher-placed noble, wincing as he saw the pain clear on the baron's face. "You say your cybernetic arm is responsible for damaging your shoulder joint on a regular basis?"

The baron nodded, grimacing. "Yes, confound the Engineers. They have a vendetta against me. Something about a duel I fought long ago..."

The Shelit nodded. He gestured to a lackey nearby. "Technician, please apply the alpha module."

The technician stepped forward and placed a gray delta-shaped object on the Baron's arm. There was a brief shimmer as what appeared to be thousands of nanobots sprung into action, streaming up the baron's arms, secreting themselves into joints, connections, and wiring. The shimmering ceased shortly thereafter, leaving behind a dull gray ash of wasted nanobots.

Dyn smiled slowly. "Now, how does it feel, Milord?"

The baron's eyebrows shot up and he got to his feet, moving the prosthetic up and down, sideways, through the full range of motion, clearly without any pain. "That's amazing! How did you...?"

"A house secret, Milord. Now, about those Li Halan weapon plans you say you have..."

The Shelit are a sly and exceedingly intelligent house who have long lain like sleeping vipers. Now they have emerged from hiding on Kurga — a barbarian world — and are clearly Hazat allies. Minor nobility on Kurga, disfavored by the Caliphate, the Shelit are hyper-rational cybernetics engineers without equal. What they lack in personality and culture, they more than make up for with their valuable, secret lore.

History of the House

Not much is known about the Shelit. They are very new to the Known Worlds, having only recently been introduced by the Hazat after they made an alliance with that major house against their traditional Kurga Caliphate rulers. They are an ingratiating, seemingly peaceful people — no known reported hostilities.

There are rumors which say that the Shelit were the product of a Second Republic genetic experiment in hyper-intelligence combined with organic cybernetics. The Shelit's culture seems wholly artificial, and certainly their hunger for knowledge is nearly inhuman. Others believe they are a plant for the Vau or of some other, heretofore unrevealed alien race. Certainly their strange customs and high intelligence seems to point toward alien involvement — that, or years of inbreeding and repression of natural human instincts.

House Culture and Ways

Socially, Shelit is a very dull, mundane house. The Shelit do not have celebrations. Their traditional dress is gray, white, or dark clothing made of simple fabrics and severe, conservative cuts. They have almost no art. Instead, their culture revolves around competitions for knowledge and the perfection of the intellect; for fun, they have memorization trials and complex mathematical contests.

There are four ranks among Shelit nobility: Doer, Maker, Talker and Thinker. Rank is designated by a number after the noble's name. Shelit names are usually only three letters long, although some rebels have four or even five. Initiation into the Shelit family responsibilities occurs when a young Shelit reaches the age of majority (18) and is ceremoniously fitted with a voluntary cybernetic replacement limb. Not all of these replacements are enhanced — most of them are normal prosthetics. Once this occurs, a Shelit is considered to be a Doer, and is assigned tasks.

There is a kind of command hierarchy: A Thinker can command a Talker, a Talker a Maker, etc.. But there are corollaries; one cannot interrupt a Doer at one job to have him do another, regardless of the priority. The local Thinker sets priority. Because these rank terms are frequently confusing to other houses, the Shelit have wisely begun the practice of adapting to Known Worlds nomenclature: a Thinker is a "Marquis" or "Marquessa"; a Talker, "Baron"; a Maker, "Baronet"; and a Doer, "Knight." Shelit will adapt any social convention to accomplish their goals, which are basically twofold: One, acquire political power; two, acquire knowledge.

An important person among the Shelit is a Rememberer. A Rememberer is very priestlike in many ways. It is the Rememberer's job to record all of the combined Shelit knowledge and memorize it, passing it on to her offspring when it comes time. Rumors have it that the as-yet-unseen "King" of the Shelit, the Remember of All Memory, is actually a complex think machine and not human at all.

Holdings

The Shelit now have a few minor fiefs within larger Hazat holdings throughout the Known Worlds, in addition to their old fief on Kurga (now in Hazat-claimed territory). They like to keep an extremely low profile. So far, few have learned of their advanced cybernetics knowledge; the house wishes to keep it this way. They are provided for by the Hazat, in exchange for the Shelit's prototypes and repair advice.

Personnel

The Shelit are incredibly narrow-minded: They are interested in technology only insofar as it can teach them about cybernetics. They are in the practice now of finding disgruntled Engineers, showing them their knowledge, and subverting them to their service — a process they call "recruiting." Their efforts now allow them to apply their highly technical knowledge to actual technology. Without technicians or engineers on Kurga, their experimentation was restricted to the abstract. Nonetheless, working with outdated equipment and ancient tools, the Shelit can still manage to make their knowledge valuable.

Leading Shelit: Sir Nin (a noted knight in Alexius's court), Lord Tov (secret envoy to Leagueheim, chief "recruiter"), Lady Maj (special technical advisor to the Decados and the Van Gelder), Ini (a smiling courtier often seen at Hazat functions, many believe he is the chief counselor to the Hazat), and Mov (a young upstart who has gained notoriety for himself on Kurga fighting alongside the Hazat).

Blessings/Curses: Cybersympathy (2 pts: +2 Redemption with cybernetics)/ Weird (+2 pts: -2 Extrovert among provincials)

Benefices/Afflictions: CyberTherapy (4 pts per cybertrait; allows the recipient to bear more cybertraits than is normally allowed — see **Forbidden Lore: Technology**, Chapter Three. The Shelit practice this therapy)/ Dispassionate (4 pts)

Background Affliction

Dispassionate (4 pts): In stressful circumstances, a Shelit may be required to roll Human + Empathy to avoid behaving in an extremely insensitive manner. If the roll fails, the Shelit may do something which, although it may seem logical to her at the time, is quite inhuman. For example, she might decide that since a baby is screaming it needs to be silenced, and throw it out a window.

Thana
(THAY-nah)

The Avestite Caramikos slapped the Thana abruptly. The Thana noble bowed his head and took the brunt of the blow, his face one of childlike innocence which made the priest's skin crawl.

"You haven't been listening to me, have you?" Caramikos said. "I have performed the necessary rites. I know that evil is here. Who among you has not reported the unclean one who dwells within?"

The gathered Thana throng did little to draw attention to themselves. An older man held his son's fist to his side in silent reproachment.

"You bear the sins of your fathers and you will always bear them," said Caramikos. "They made the choice to alter their basic structures. I join with other voices in the Church in claiming that you are no human creatures as far as I can see. Look at you! Unaging, undeveloped. Your eyes — violet! Your hair nearly translucent! Spawn of Evil, I say. You may look like Empyreans, but you are devils most sure. You must always be watched, I say. Yes, watched. And monitored. And if you take one misstep — even one! — you will be dealt with most severely." As if in illustration, the man turned and barked at his underling. "Bring in the Hound of the Light!"

The doors parted and many Thana turned their heads to the floor as they saw the Hound — bound in an ugly iron psychic inhibitor, dragged forward naked. She was a Thana, her youthful appearance unbroken by years under the lash and the cleansing fire, but the light behind her eyes was subhuman. Caramikos put his hand down to her cheek and she lapped at his palm gratefully.

"I must admit, however... you and your kind do have some uses..."

Once gentle, now deadly, the Thana are an angelic looking, long-lived house from a Lost World. Their tendency to exhibit psychic powers has made them the subject of continuous persecution. Still, their natural ability to rule and the natural tendency of others to obey them has kept them two steps ahead of genocide.

History of the House

Descendants of early Diaspora settlers, the Thana come from a world called Eridol, which was lost (its jumpgate accidentally sealed) before the rise of the Second Republic. On Eridol, the Thana, leaders of the human colony, were worshipped as living gods by the semisentient native creatures called the Aluun. Eridol was rediscovered during the latter days of the Republic — just when an Aluun uprising threatened to destroy the Thana. They were given safe passage off Eridol, but the jumpgate was sealed again by rebels before the colony could be fully evacuated. The Thana became a family without a world. Tracing their lineage back to Mediterranean royalty, they were immediately besieged with offers from Known Worlds noble families, seeking alliances for the coming war — or scapegoats to throw to the angry populace.

The Phavian Institute discovered that Thana family members had a tremendous potential for psionics and worked to help them develop it. When the Republic fell, their noble allies granted them land and peasants throughout the Known Worlds, but their reputation for psionics won them the attention of the purging flame of the Church.

As a result, the Thana have been persecuted wherever they have found themselves. Frequently their natural charm is used as "proof" that they are psychic. The Church is nervous when they witness peasants loyally fighting and dying for lords not even of their homeworlds. While this loyalty is engendered through non-psychic means, the Church wants to believe otherwise.

For a time, Thana scions were confined to reservations and ghettos, bound by psi-inhibitors and safely watched. When Emperor Vladimir issued the General Reclamation and Reformation Act in a move to mollify the Ur-Obun who had helped him to power, the act was applied to all aliens and psychics. The Thana were finally allowed to leave their prisons and intermingle once again with society, many returning to the fiefs from which they were once evicted.

House Culture and Ways

Because the Thana are long lived, they value life. This has in the past caused them to take a very pacifistic and nonviolent approach. However, in these dark times, many Thana youth have turned their beautiful bodies into killing machines. Tall and almost avian in their bone structure, the Thana make for excellent fencers and have an uncanny knack for second-guessing their opponents.

As a result of their well-known wisdom in many areas, and because of their talents with people, they often serve as advisors to certain Royal Houses. It is also whispered that they have made pacts of secret alliance with the Li Halan and the Juandaastas, and are frequently friends with Eskatonic priests (this has done little to protect them from the Avestites).

Although Thana is by and large a poor house, its members rarely must work to obtain what they need — they frequently find themselves with wealthy patrons who simply wish them to serve as pretty things in their household, living relics of a past time. Even those Thana who are not so "lucky" are usually well-supported by philanthropists who feel good about providing them a living and rectifying past injustices.

There is a kind of cool arrogance about the Thana. It is not hard to imagine them being worshipped as gods — they are just as selfish and prideful as any deity. They are elitist and distant. The Thana are creators of many popular works of art and poetry, although they disdain their common following.

They rule themselves chiefly by dint of age. The Eldest of an area is the highest local lord. This has created a kind of stratification among the Thana as they have been allowed to breed unchecked in recent years and are now experiencing a "boom" of Thanic adolescents who have yet to even reach their first score of years. The Eldest counsels nonviolence, while the young ones are warriors, fighting for the respect others will not give freely.

Holdings

Thanic Manors are rare, as many Thana lost their fiefs during their initial persecution. However, some Thana have managed to reclaim the holdings originally awarded them during Divestiture, and some have been granted new fiefs. Visitors to these lands are often quite suprised to find how peaceful and well-run they are. Despite continuous persecution, the Thana are canny leaders. Some still secretly exist in ghettoes on various worlds, mistreated and ill-used by their jailers. If the Thana leaders knew of the existence of these lost family members, they would be quick to free them — regardless of who they anger doing so.

Personnel

Thana make excellent courtiers and effective nobles. They are premium-quality artists and sculptors, and philosophers and academics as well. Young Thana find their hawklike reflexes serve them well as soldiers, even if their beautiful appearances mean they are thought of as weak. Most Thana receive schooling from their patrons and are usually very knowledgeable.

While most psychic Thana have a degree of immunity from Church prosecution due to their noble status, many who are caught in crimes using their powers are frequently forced to become Penitent "Hounds of the Light," used by the Inquisition to sniff out psychics hiding in the Known Worlds.

Leading Thana: Morik Danae (Chief Penitent Hound of the Light for Temple Avesti), Alarun Silal (the Eldest of the Eldest, the oldest known living Thana who is now 212 years old by the Imperial Calendar), Mari Halor (philosopher and cultural leader to the young Thana who are now coming into their own)

Typical Thana Traits

Characteristics: Dexterity, Psi
Natural skills: Impress, Observe
Learned skills: Etiquette, Focus, Inquiry, Lore (Politics), Speak Eridol (Urthish dialect), Stoic Mind
Blessings/Curses: Angelic (3 pts: +3 Charm among humans)/ Guilty (+2 pts: -2 on all rolls when opposing Church officials)
Benefices: Riches (7 pts maximum), Long Lived (5 pts)

Background Benefice

Long Lived (5 pts): While all Thana seem to live longer than most humans by 10–20 years, some have a genetic predisposition to much longer life, up to twice the normal human life span.

Torenson
(TOR-en-sun)

"No, milord, if you seat the duchess next to a mere knight, the scandal-mongers will justifiably call you a boor! Better leave this one to me. I sha'n't disappoint you — or make you look the fool!" Leif Torenson smiled as the proud Hazat lord nodded meekly in acquiescence. Power truly came in many forms.

After almost becoming an extinct line, House Torenson is again on the rise due to a clever campaign to have its members recognized as the authorities on matters of etiquette. Most become tutors and trainers to young members of the five royal houses, while some act as advisors to heads of families or lesser nobles, worming their way into their confidence, learning their secrets, encouraging them to utilize perfect etiquette and always, always knowing what is the correct response in any social situation. They have become indispensable to those whom they advise. Only a few of those they serve truly understand

how much power they hold.

There are many jokes that concern the Torensons, emphasizing their rigid social rules (most of which feature amusing bedroom tales). No one would deny, however, that their attention to detail and intimate knowledge of even the smallest rules of etiquette have saved social situations that might otherwise have been disastrous. They are in great demand when planning any sort of social function, from business meetings to grand balls, royal feasts, clandestine trysts, recreational hunts, elaborate weddings (and any pre-nuptial agreements hammered out), parlays between warring parties, and even funerals. Knowing what sort of event is planned often means they have important information and can make investments accordingly. Their on-scene presence to keep affairs running smoothly likewise makes them some of the best informed people in the Known Worlds. Torensons travel in the best social circles and charge exorbitant rates for both their expertise and discretion.

History of the House

House Torenson traces its lineage back to the Scandinavian nations on Holy Terra. Citing its role in the colonization of the Known Worlds, Torenson can justifiably claim its share of glory. Among the first to reach many new worlds, it claimed three worlds for its own. When it discovered that it didn't have the manpower to take full advantage of all its planets and believed that it would soon be at war with the al-Malik, House Torenson negotiated an alliance with House Keddah, gaining Keddah's promised support in exchange for the planet of Shaprut.

Soon thereafter, still fearing war from the al-Malik, Torenson pledged fealty to House Dextrite rather than face war on two possible fronts. The house almost became extinct (along with several other minor houses) during Vladimir's wars. Its planets were seized and Torenson had no soldiers with which to gain them back. Interestingly, when the al-Malik declared war on the Masseri, who had subsumed House Dextrite, Torenson's old allies the Keddah were drawn into war due to their pledge to Torenson, who were still bound to Dextrite. Torenson itself was only nominally involved, since it had no soldiers and no holdings left.

Emilia Torenson's impassioned speech declaring her family's neutrality and citing dozens of social conventions to back their stance won admiration from most of the noble houses and assured her family places by many of their leaders' sides. It became fashionable to have a Torenson as a social advisor and tutor in social graces. Now there is hardly a court in the Known Worlds that lacks a Torenson counselor.

House Culture and Ways

Torenson pride in its members expertise extends to their modes of dress, speech and behavior. They always dress appropriately to both their station and the demands of the situation, advising their noble patrons likewise. The greatest fear of any Torenson is to commit any sort of faux pas; most would rather commit suicide. Rank within the house (other than that held by Marquessa Agneta Torenson, who inherited the title) is accorded based on respect garnered through social triumphs. Thus a successful major domo working for House Hazat might be given the title of baron after a particularly clever social coup. Outside the family, many Torensons have been granted various noble ranks by those nobles whom they serve. The most successful of these is Duke Halvard Torenson, who is married to Duchess Matilde Hazat.

The Torensons claim to have no enemies and insist that all people with social graces are their allies. They hold no territories of their own, though they are often asked to manage various estates whose rulers have not yet come of age. Unlike the Masseri, whose landless status prejudices many against them, Torenson's lack of property is seen as an asset by their employers, and they are greatly respected as neutral social advisors. The only workers Torenson employs are personal servants and bodyguards, usually free people with good manners and the sense to remain silent and in the background unless summoned.

Leading Torensons: Marquessa Agneta Torenson (head of the house, advisor to Alexius Hawkwood), Bishop Magnus Torenson (Orthodox instructor in Church etiquette), Hemming Torenson (seneschal of House Hazat on Aragon).

Typical Torenson Traits
Characteristics: Wits, Perception
Natural skills: Charm, Observe
Learned skills: Bureaucracy, Etiquette, Lore (Noble customs), Read Urthish, Social (Oratory)
Blessings/Curses: Elan (2 pts: +2 Etiquette at high society functions)/ Indignant (+2 pts: -2 Charm in rude situations)
Benefices: Gossip Network, Protection

Trusnikron
(TROOZ-ni-KRON)

Ginevra threw herself onto the urroc's back, grasping its neck ruff for reins. "Race you—" she called back over her shoulder to Vivienna Hawkwood as her magnificent steed thrust off from the clifftop and into the thermal updraft. "Not fair!" Vivienna shouted — she was now riding upside down, clinging to her mount by the barest handful of feathers a thousand feet from the ground below. "You're a beast master, the damn bird won't let YOU fall!"

Only a step above barbarism at one time, the Trusnikron made their name as cavalry officers and beast tamers and trainers. Members of this aggressive, young house seem to have an affinity for creatures of all sorts. They train warbeasts, riding animals and racers for use by the Great Houses. They themselves choose to serve as cavalry officers with the Hawkwoods, who recognize

Trusnikron's strict code of honor as similar to their own. They also relish service in the Kurga Conflict as mercenaries for House Hazat, whose prowess in battle they greatly admire. No Trusnikron would dream of fighting dishonorably when facing honorable foes; likewise they have no trouble throwing honor out with the dishwater when opposing dishonorable foes.

Straightforward, even brutal at times, House Trusnikron raises children who are tough, self-reliant, resourceful and nearly fearless. Members take great pride in their family and accomplishments, and refuse to acknowledge that anyone outside the family rides any beast better than they do. Somewhat like the Hazat, the Trusnikron are always looking for evidence of new beasts, though to tame them rather than fight them. Amazing judges of horse (and other beast) flesh, the Trusnikron's estimation concerning a beast's value is unquestionable. If a noble wants a horse, urroc, lyocel or even a ravening guernicabeast tamed to the saddle and trained for battle or sport, he is insane if he looks to any trainer outside the Trusnikron. Whether others are as adept at such training or not is beside the question. Trusnikron training is perceived to be the best available and few nobles have the knowledge themselves to challenge that.

History of the House

Trusnikron mythology holds that their ancestors arose from a combination of Cossack and gypsy blood, a rather unlikely combination for nobles. Those who question them or insult their ancestors, however, end up on the wrong end of a flux sword, so most simply nod and agree that their pedigrees are among the best. Some also claim that their real ancestors were offshoots from the Knights Templar living in Scotland, who followed the Hawkwoods into space. Whatever the truth of the matter, House Trusnikron nobles have always boasted of their prowess as cavalry officers and saw no reason to change just because the local fauna ran more toward gigantic birds, orange dolphins or fanged camels.

While they have established home territories on almost every settled world, they rarely claim more than a small area near the natural habitat of the animals they seek to tame. Whereas they train animals for every Royal House, they serve as troops only for the Hawkwoods and Hazat. Because they are well connected to just about everyone, they have suffered little from the changing fortunes that plague almost every other minor house.

House Culture and Ways

The Trusnikron, while they have garnered noble status for themselves, are not as adept as the older houses at scheming and backstabbing, which is why the Hawkwoods like and respect them — though they rarely treat them as social equals. To those who fight alongside them, the Trusnikron are, in many ways, more like favored family retainers than a separate noble house.

House Trusnikron gives House Torenson nightmares. Gruff, honest, plainly-spoken, they rarely pay attention to more than the basic niceties, seeing etiquette as little more than foolish claptrap meant to obscure people's true feelings. They wear colorful clothing or riding leathers, furs and feathers. Often, they smell of the beasts they train, a smell they consider both honest and noble. They despise the perfumed court life in which liars and schemers are listened to with more attention than those who speak truthfully and passionately.

The bluff, affable Trusnikron, though granted noble status and titles, choose to refer to themselves either by their military ranks or by their own titles. Master Tamer (Marquis), Trainer (Baron), Rider (Baronet) and Hand (Knight) are the ranks they recognize, though their lowest rank — Hand — usually denotes a young member who may ride better than many nobles who've been instructed in the art for years. Rising in rank seems to be a matter of impressing one's fellow family members with particularly brave feats or riding exhibitions, though sometimes they "create" ranks to deal with unwanted customers. Thus a mere Hand may be given the title Grand Marquis in order to refuse to train a Decados warbeast. That such titles mean nothing is a source of great amusement to the Trusnikron.

The Trusnikron say they have no enemies, just honorable and dishonorable allies and acquaintances. As the full displeasure of both House Hawkwood and House Hazat would fall upon anyone who harmed the Trusnikron, and as most nobles know few other experts who can train their valuable beasts, this is probably true. Among their allies, they count Hawkwood, Juandaastas, Justinian and Hazat. Most of the other houses, great or minor, are considered acquaintances. All Decados are seen as dishonorable and potential enemies, and they reserve a special hell for the Van Gelder, whom they despise with every fiber of their beings.

Holdings

Trusnikron have holdings on many worlds, but the best known are an urroc preserve on Ravenna, a lyocel ranch on Cadavus and a station on Pyre, where they train grolla crawlers. They often prefer temporary camps to stationary buildings, so they can move with nomadic animal herds and learn their ways.

Personnel

The Trusnikron don't believe in keeping serfs or slaves. They work alongside Hawkwood serfs and utilize the other houses' workers when necessary, but they are uncomfortable with keeping others in bondage. They consider the beasts they tame to be partners. Trusnikron-trained beasts that are mistreated often mysteriously disappear, usually in concert with some costly property damage inflicted on the cruel "owner." The family has ties to crafters who make saddles and bridles, utilizing their understanding of their beasts to create the most comfortable,

beautifully decorated and long-wearing equipment available. A saddle with the Trusnikron name on it sells for twice to three times that of any other.

Leading Trusnikrons: Master Tamer Kesare Trusnikron (head of the family, master of cavalry for House Hawkwood), Trainer Aurelne Trusnikron (mistress of leviathans on Madoc), Trainer Jervais Trusnikron (head of mercenary forces employed by House Hazat).

Typical Trusnikron Traits
Characteristics: Strength, Dexterity, Extrovert
Natural skills: Dodge, Fight, Impress, Vigor
Learned skills: Beast Lore, Drive Beastcraft, Lore (one or more animals), Ride
Blessings/Curses: Xeno Equestrian (4 pts: +4 Ride to offset the -4 penalty for riding an unfamiliar type of beast)/ Uncouth (+2 pts: -2 Extrovert at society functions)
Benefices: Beast Barding (1 pt: 4 + 4d plate armor)

Van Gelder
(van GELD-ur)

He wondered who she could be. Lovely, cultured, obviously well-educated, she glided with him across the dance floor, seeming almost to float. That she was noble, he had no doubt, but he couldn't place her house. Torenson? al-Malik? Perhaps he would ask her when he invited her up to his lodgings. Then he felt the blade slip between his ribs and the numbing poison begin to take effect. As he slid to the floor, he realized which house was hers. She had to be Van Gelder.

Once a major player in the power games of the Known Worlds, Van Gelder lost most of its clout along with its sons in Vladimir's wars. Before their alliance with House Decados, most people thought of the Van Gelder as jumped-up merchants playing at nobility. Many still do. Their mistake. Where the Van Gelder once cared almost exclusively for wealth, they have changed their goals. Allied to Decados in order to survive, Van Gelder has learned hard lessons and found a new calling — espionage and assassination.

History of the House

Though by no means pioneers, this coalition of Dutch, Swiss, and Belgian zaibatsu came through the jumpgate from Urth as soon as it was safe to do so. Foreseeing the demise of the First Republic, the corporation claimed several outlying planets, intermarried, and House Van Gelder (named for the CEO) was born. Some time thereafter, it emerged as one of the great noble houses. Its ties to industry and noble alike served it well until Vladimir united all the houses against the barbarians.

Vladimir failed to keep his promises to several of those who supported him, among them, the Van Gelder. The house rose in revolt; Vladimir seized its planets and holdings. After a bloody war, Van Gelder and the others were forced to surrender, stripped of all they owned and obliged to throw themselves on the mercy of the Decados in order to survive. Angered by Vladimir's betrayal, the Van Gelder swore never again to be at the mercy of rulers.

Before this time, the Van Gelders had been thought of as bland and unmemorable. After it, they became even more so. Only now they deliberately used their blandness to hide in plain sight. While they rarely opt for the face-altering cosmetic surgeries popular among certain Decados, many people have trouble recalling their features even after spending a good deal of time in their company. They have linked this with a heretofore unacknowledged talent for mimicking other noble families, allowing them to excel as spies and assassins. The Van Gelder perform these missions for the Decados (and other employers) as well as managing some of the Decados moneys and estates.

House Culture and Ways

The Van Gelder are mostly overlooked. Those who know them well, however, understand that they are consumed by anger and bitterness for the near-death of their family. Most Van Gelder have little sense of joy or humor and little time for anything but their duties. If anything ever gives away the Van Gelder, it is their solemnity. In the wake of Vladimir's betrayal, they trust no one and have no respect for so-called honor. They are master poisoners. To the Van Gelder, everyone is either a paying customer or a target. They have become much like a ninja family in that they obey their leader, even when individual members feel that they cannot condone the rest of their family's activities.

Those who refuse to act as covert operatives usually end up managing estates or seek their fortunes elsewhere. But all follow their unwritten code of silence regarding their family's actions. House rank is awarded through merit and abiding by the code.

When not on a job, the Van Gelder live lives of luxury surrounded by fine art, clothed in fashionable, rich attire and served the best food that Decados money can buy. Their code requires active "agents" (as they call themselves) to leave such accommodations after no more than a month and return to "work quarters" where they train for their next (or ongoing) assignment.

Almost no one realizes he is an enemy of the Van Gelder until it is too late. The house's only real allies are the Decados — and only for so long as the Van Gelder prove useful.

Holdings

Van Gelder managers maintain several valuable holdings for the Decados on Cadiz, but their most important holdings are on Malignatius, where they have waged a very successful campaign to keep religious malcontents fighting among themselves rather than against the Decados.

Personnel

The Decados have provided House Van Gelder with serfs, slaves, and guards, to be used as they see fit. Serfs and slaves usually farm or fish, providing the family with sustenance. Guards are used to provide extra security at their residences, but no Van Gelder actually trusts those provided by Decados. They are placed in non-essential positions and ignored. Van Gelder agents handle the real security.

Leading Van Gelders: Kaatje Van Gelder (head of the currently working agents), Zacharia Van Gelder (head of the family), Hendrik Van Gelder (a.k.a. Marquis Adam Hawkwood, a.k.a. Lord Josef Hazat, a.k.a. Deacon Kadar Li Halan, a.k.a. Countess Adara al-Malik, a.k.a....)

Typical Van Gelder Traits

Characteristics: Wits, Perception
Natural skills: Charm, Impress, Observe, Sneak
Learned skills: Disguise, Etiquette, Inquiry, Knavery, Social (Acting), Streetwise
Blessings/Curses: Chameleon (3 pts: +2 Knavery and +1 Acting)/ Alienated (+2 pts: -2 to Extrovert without guise)
Benefices/Afflictions: Family Ties (3 pts)/ Infamous Family (1 pt)

Xanthippe
(ZAN-theep)

"I've come to offer you some very favorable deals with our house..." Kiley smiled, her gray eyes glittering under her court garb hood.

"With the Xanthippe?" the fat older noble Baron Tregaron said, smiling as he stepped to the window. "For what? I don't need any more warriors. And if I did, I could just get them from the Muster. And I can buy your wine from anyone."

"For two very good reasons, my Lord Tregaron. The first is that we offer the finest quality soldiers and the best wine in the Known Worlds..."

The baron began to interrupt.

"...the second is that I have pictures of you with a young lady who is certainly, most definitely, not Lady Tregaron." Kiley whispered, leaning close to him.

His eyes filled with understanding. "Oh. I see. I understand now. Yes...those are excellent terms. Where do I press my signet?"

The Xanthippe are cunning, wise, and fiercely independent. Small of stature but tough, they have continuously won and rewon their nobility through trickery, through solidarity, and from the silent support of the peasants whom they rule. A matriarchal house, its members have relied upon their wits, their intuition, and their natural knack for social weaving to keep their fortunes afloat.

History of the House

The Xanthippe proudly trace their lineage back to one of Urth's first space colonies, on the sacred orb called Luna. Their foremothers were among the first to migrate from Earth during the Diaspora. The Xanthippe have been excellent survivors throughout history; they claim their traditions and customs to be relatively unchanged from their days as a Lunar Enclave. This internal consistency is due to the Measure, a written work which serves as religious text, folkways writing, body of law, history, and social customs reference — a work which is held in the strictest confidence.

The Xanthippe Speakers and their Great Mother are historically among the most politically savvy people in the Known Worlds — it is their cunning which has kept the Xanthippe out of the way of the larger houses while maintaining their own grip on survival. The Xanthippe prefer to be social chameleons, staying unnoticed in the larger picture, while certainly making their influence felt in areas that count.

Of particular interest to history is the fact that many conflicts could well have fallen a different way if not for the sudden arrival of Xanthippe elite mercenaries — they have been frequently used by other houses as "hole cards" to be played as a last-ditch effort or as a final coup.

House Culture and Ways

The center of Xanthippe life is the Moonhaven, a special secured area they create for themselves, governed by the Measure. Each Moonhaven is exactly the same throughout the Known Worlds. The Moonhaven is the central operations center for the Xanthippe's two main profit centers: mercenaries and wine.

There is very little fat among the Xanthippe. All members of the house are expected to work, to fight, and to provide support to their vassals. By age five, Xanthippe girls have learned the basics of hand-to-hand combat, while their brothers have learned basic first aid and the preliminaries of wine-growing.

A matriarchal house, they were at one time plagued with separatist sexist leanings. A social revolution among the men in the house (who refused to care for the children or bring in the grapes that season) caused an end to most sexual discrimination. Now men are trusted alongside their sisters, although many still do not rise to positions of political power, and by custom they are still denied the title of Speaker. As a sidenote, despite their particularly stringent battle training and the fact that their men are just as vicious at war as their women, there are no reported incidences of rape among the Xanthippe. In general, female Xanthippe are trained to be leaders, warriors, and policy makers from birth, while the men are encouraged to become artisans, healers, caretakers, and protectors of children.

The Xanthippe remain culturally and genetically pure by their fairly strict code concerning marriage outside their house. Xanthippe of one Moonhaven are frequently fostered out to a far distant Moonhaven upon reaching majority.

They don't particularly go in for dueling, although they are certain to answer any challenges with great ferocity.

Rumormongering is held as a high art to the Xanthippe. From an early age children are encouraged to snoop and report what they know. As a result, it is a widespread practice which provides the Xanthippe with critical information they need.

Holdings

The Xanthippe are small in number, but their tightly disciplined members are spread far and wide. Their Moonhaven on Aragon is their largest, Cadavus has the most overworked Moonhaven, and the most medically advanced is on Leagueheim. Many Xanthippe dwell on moons throughout the Known Worlds under pressure bubbles built during the Second Republic, utilizing freely available solar energy to grow their famous grapes. Male Xanthippe are often trained as lunarbase technicians, and are sought out as such by other houses seeking to maintain living cities on their own moons. Xanthippe are sometimes given a portion of these lunar lands in return for upkeeping entire colonies.

Personnel

There is no room for the lazy among the Xanthippe. Each member of the house is assigned three duties: work to be done, a person or place to defend in time of battle, and vassals to administer. They frequently learn many different skills throughout their lifetimes and have a reputation for being well-rounded. Each Moonhaven has a Speaker's Circle which is the advisory committee to the Moonhavener who ultimately rules. The Moonhavener answers to the Speaker for her area of the Known Worlds, who answers in turn to the Great Mother, chosen by consensus from among the Speakers, usually to rule for life (although the Measure has customs which dictate when the Mother might step down).

All Xanthippe now spend time in military training (although in the past the men were not allowed). It is considered a dishonor to require a bodyguard, although Speakers frequently carry with them a squad of elite warriors.

Despite the fact that the Xanthippe are mercenaries they will not work for just anyone able to fill their purses

with coin. They frequently reject missions that are too dangerous, too foolhardy, or which are against the best interests of the Xanthippe as a whole.

Leading Xanthippe: Great Mother Dora Azariah, Speaker Kiley (of Aragon), Alexandra Rhys (famous Xanthippe sculptress and general), Genevieve Tiercel (Speaker of War Services and skilled diplomat), Shandra Laval (famous vintner and developer of several radiation-resistant strains of grapes)

Typical Xanthippe Traits

Characteristics: Dexterity, Endurance

Natural skills: Impress, Melee, Shoot, Sneak, Vigor

Learned skills: Academia, Etiquette, Read Urthish, Remedy, Social (Leadership), Stoic Body, Warfare (Military Tactics)

Blessings/Curses: Disciplined (2 pts: +2 Calm in combat situations)/ Condescending (+2 pts: -2 Extrovert among non-Xanthippe)

Benefices: Measure Consultation (3 pts)

Background Benefice

Measure Consultation (3 pts): The character has a copy of the Measure — the great Xanthippe guideline book — which she carries around with her (+2 points for a handheld computer consulter). Because of the vast nature of this sprawling work, it is likely that the character can find relevant advise or information for just about any situation. Roll Wits + Academia to find anything of value for the situation at hand. A failed roll does not necessarily mean there is no good advice — just that the character has failed to find the right section of the book.

Emblems of the Minor Houses:

Juandaastas

Masseri

Justinian

Shelit

Keddah

Thana

 Torenson

 Trusnikron

 Xanthippe

 Van Gelder

Exiles Among Their Kind: Alien Lords

by Bill Bridges

Ur-Obun

"Who is first among you?" demanded Count Tchaivsky of House Decados, impatient already with his stay on Obun. He had finally been granted audience with a preliminary council, and five Ur-Obun councilors looked at him, clearly perplexed by his question. Then, one of them nodded and motioned toward the oldest among them, one who was surely in his later years, judging from his weak shuffle and wrinkled face.

"Lon roaJadd is the eldest among us," the Obun said. "He was born before all of us."

"That's not what I meant!" the flustered Decados yelled. "Who among you is the highest in peerage? Who holds the most rank?"

Again, the blank stares. Then, the Obun spoke again: "As I said, Lon roaJadd is eldest. He is thus wisest and highest in our esteem. Then there is Jovan Vanan voLarn," he motioned toward a much younger Obun, "who has gained much respect through her diplomacy in the Reyvik Accord. But we are all councilors, and have each been sent to aid you with your problem."

The count sighed. He should have anticipated this. He was warned, after all. These weaklings had no one of better breeding among them — they were all commoners. Fools, in fact. It required a pack of them to decide on issues that were best judged by one noble of superior breeding.

The Obun gathered about him frowned and looked politely away. Count Tchaivsky frowned himself, puzzled at the sudden reaction. Then he sucked in his breath in embarrassment, mentally stammering out some apology. Fools, perhaps, *he thought,* but psychics as well.

The Chosen of the Gods

The Ur-Obun used to have a noble class, made up of a privileged few supposedly descended from the Chosen of the Gods. When the gods (commonly viewed now as the Anunnaki, or Ur-races) withdrew from the affairs of mortals, they named some of their most favored Ur-Obun to lead over others. These mortal lords removed themselves from the populace to contemplate metaphysics and philosophy unhindered by material concerns. The nobles' disinterest in the affairs of the people, coupled with an idealistic philosophy which filtered from them to the people, gave birth to a broad egalitarianism among the populace. In the absence of leadership from the Chosen, the people learned to lead themselves — to the ultimate doom of the noble estate.

It was not only a rising tide of egalitarianism which dethroned the untouchables; their own customs also killed them. Imbued early on with powerful feelings of superiority, the nobles refused to breed with those they deemed inferior, and began a breeding program which became increasingly discriminating until only those nobles with close family ties were considered acceptable partners. Ignoring the evidence of inbreeding, the noble populace diminished in size.

In addition, they imposed a societal distance from their subjects which blinded them to the problems suffered by their people. This distance only increased with each generation, until most nobles ruled from afar, not even comprehending the decrees they made and unaware that, in most provinces, their dictates were ignored. The people instead developed small, autonomous communities which eventually bonded together into a worldwide federation and excluded the nobles from power.

The nobles intially resisted when they realized their disenfranchisement, but this was over practically before it began, for even their own householders had become federates. The Chosen were too important historically and religiously to be abolished, but they were henceforth kept from any decision making. Funded by the Federation, they continued to live in their lavish mansions on the mountains, far from the sight of the people.

The Last of the Chosen

The story of the last noble of Obun is still told today, as a cautionary tale for those who grow too headstrong in their ways. Duke Aniki voPohjoli went mad after his beloved wife was killed in an earthquake. Desperate to find some meaning in her death, he studied plate tectonics with a fervor that astonished his contemporaries. His theories revealed certain terraforming laws well before humans later discovered them. His studies convinced him, however, that a cataclysm threatened Obun, a tremor which would rock the entire planet, shift it from its orbit and send it hurtling into the sun. But his "proofs" fell on deaf ears. No one wanted to listen to such apocalyptic rants.

Desperate that at least one Obun survive the coming disaster, he strapped his infant son, the last noble heir of a line once ordained by the gods, into a rocket and shot him into space, toward a distant star once said to be the home of the gods. There, the last Obun would be raised by the gods to one day sow the seeds of the race anew (with another godling, it was assumed).

Aniki waited. Nothing happened. The cataclysm never came. Years passed, and Aniki finally realized his madness — which drove him madder still. Convinced that he had killed his only son, he desperately pleaded with his fellow Obun to search space for the tiny rocket. The Federation had only recently achieved sufficient space travel to begin colonization of the solar system. They humored the old man and used their most powerful telescopes, but found no sign of the rocket. Instead, they detected a jumpgate, well past the orbit of their farthest satellite.

Driven mad with shame and remorse, Duke Leroj jumped off a mountain mere hours before the first human ship entered the Obun system to drag the Ur-Obun into an interstellar world of conflict.

The Ruling Council

The Obun Federation is made up of many locally autonomous colonies. The sole purpose of the Federation was once to oversee the interactions and commerce between colonies, with no power to rule over the colonies themselves, except when one colony threatened the autonomy of another. This role changed once interstellar travel became possible and Obun joined the Known Worlds as one world among many. Now the Federation has the power to supersede colony control when interstellar issues intervene.

Each colony elects a councilor to sit on the Ruling Council, although this candidate must then pass the Ordeal before she is accepted. If the candidate fails the test, another must be chosen.

The Ordeal

The Ordeal holds much cultural and even religious significance among the Obun. It is descended from a similar ritual once performed by a small religious sect which worshipped the ancient gods. The Ordeal was designed to mimic many of the trials once undertaken by the gods themselves as they fought their way to the heights of cosmic power.

Today, the Ordeal has three separate contests: physical, mental and spiritual. The physical test is usually once of endurance rather than vigor, often involving a long hike up a mountain or a marathon through the applicant's colony. It actually tests willpower more than physical fitness. It is said that in the old days, this was a trial by combat.

The mental portion tests learning and education. The applicant is asked a barrage of questions by a Locutor, a councilor sent to the local colony to administer the Ordeal. The test is oral rather than written, and the questions must be answered without hesitation.

The spiritual portion is administered by a priest, most often from the Ven Lohji sect, but sometimes from the Bintaru faith (once the widespread religion of the Obun, before the Church displaced it). It tests the candidates' moral and ethical character with a surprise task which can be presented at anytime during the Ordeal — during the physical or mental portions, or sometime before the Ordeal has even begun. It is put to the candidate without his knowing, and his reaction is carefully watched. For instance, the candidate may come across a staged vehicle accident where people are injured. How quickly and how well he reacts to help the victims is important.

Once the Ordeal is over, the results are considered by the Locutor, the priest and the previous Councilor for that colony. If they deem the candidate did well, he is accepted.

Many Ur-Obun claim that the Ordeal is weak, a shadow of its original form, where Obun applicants would often die during the test. But the content of the original Ordeal is lost to history, for it was part of a Mystery Cult which did not record its tests for posterity.

The Role of the Council

Since the Ruling Council normally has limited powers of coercion over the individual colonies, the most valuable skill for a councilor is diplomacy — she must succeed with words where others might use force. Obun society, even though divided into villagelike colonies, is amazingly homogenous. This is due mainly to its incredibly stable societal customs, which remained largely unchanged since they were first inculcated into the Ur-Obun by the Anunnaki. With the power of divine law, these customs remain similar over the entire planet.

The very stability of these traditions once threatened the freedom of people, almost choking them with strict taboos, and would surely have lead to an oligarchic dictatorship by the Council had it not been for the reforms of Ven Lohji, disciple of the Prophet. Her Obun branch of the Universal Church, so different from the Church erected by Palamedes, reinvigorated the philosophical life

Population Control

Among the many factors contributing to the success of Obun socialism is a small populace. The religious wars of the Dark Ages, waged by the Church against the Obun, greatly reduced the population, which has yet to rise to pre-war levels. In addition, the ancient eugenics programs of the past instilled into Obun culture the idea that procreation should be a planned event, not a casual accident. Preventive pregnancy technologies are advanced on Obun, from local, handcrafted prophylactics to high tech drugs and surgery, most of them without side effects.

However, the Obun claim that their sex drive is not the obsessive, consuming impulse it seems to be in some humans. Thanks to the spiritual techniques handed down to them by their gods — techniques practiced from the cradle to grave — they have conquered their instincts. While these practices seem to have been developed specifically to harness the psychic Urge and prevent its eclipse of the psyche, they have also colored all Ur-Obun culture and society.

Others say that the Anunnaki "screwed with their skulls" and somehow programmed the drive out of them. Whether the cause is self-trained or genetically engineered, critics say that the deprogramming is failing, and they point to the increasing occurrence of violent criminals among the Obun, from rapists to serial killers. For now, most Obun blame such crimes on outside taints, and on increasing ignorance among the younger generations of Obun traditions, although some believe it comes from too long a repression of natural instincts.

of the colonies. A new age of learning and spiritual questioning began. Old, stifling forms were replaced by fresh, thoughtful ways inspired by the words of the Prophet.

Blessed with the restraint of the Prophet's powerful new ethical system, and tempered by the compassionate animism of the old Bintaru religion, the Ruling Council became a model governing body, in many ways the realization of a liberal ideal long in coming.

Nonetheless, with the coming of the intergalactic age and the rule of outside parties (House Hawkwood and others), the Ruling Council, and thus the Federation, has gained increasing power over the individual colonies. Some believe that this unique Obun form of socialism can only endure with the protection and aid of House Hawkwood. Indeed, in those times when the house's resources were placed elsewhere (such as during the Barbarian Invasions), the Hazat and other minor houses made successful claims to some Obun lands.

Virtues of a Councilmember

The Council is a meritocracy. The varying degrees of rank within its body are determined by deed or age (which is equated with wisdom). While the service is voluntary, once elected, the title of councilor lasts for life even after the councilor retires from active participation in Council affairs. (Many a time the Council has witnessed a wild swing vote when an old retiree returned for an important issue.)

Certain councilors are recognized by Known Worlders as diplomats and are treated like nobility when they are off-world. Such an intergalactic post is voluntary but requires an appointment from the Hawkwood lords who nominally rule Obun.

Rank Benefice

Similar to the noble peerage of humans, an Obun councilor has degrees of rank to consider. However, the gulf between ranks is not so deep or wide; wisdom is recognized in the small as well as the large.

3 = Umo (Federate)
5 = Votan (Notable)
7 = Jovan (Honorable)
9 = Mwerro (Advisor)
11 = roa (Mentor, prefix added to family name)
13 = Han (Sage, prefix added to family name)

Priests, from both the Ven Lohji sect of the Universal Church and the local Bintaru religion, can become councilors.

Holdings

Obun is owned by House Hawkwood, and most Ur-Obun are considered its vassals, although they are left mostly to their own devices. Some fiefs are owned by the Hazat, and a few others are owned by some minor houses (such as Juandaastas). These fiefs were once autonomous colonies; their inhabitants either moved elsewhere of became serfs for the new lords. It is considered extremely bad form to force an Obun into serfdom, but debts all too often allow human lords to do this. Most of the serfs on noble lands are nonetheless human colonists.

In many ways, Ur-Obun live in more freedom than most humans on other worlds. This is because House Hawkwood has made it a point of honor to defend their way of life, based on a pact made long ago. The pact was once broken during fighting with the Decados, when that family was allowed to seize some land from the Hawkwood to great shame. But the lands were eventually won back, and the house leaders no longer allow the duchies on Obun to be gambled in matters of honor.

The Ven Lohji sect of the Church also has a lot of power in negotiating Obun freedom of determination. Guilt from the mass deaths suffered in the religious war with the Orthodox sect during the Dark Ages has given them a lot of moral power.

Finally, Ur-Obun technology is unique. While it is no more advanced than most human technology, it follows different principles, based on Anunnaki intervention long ago. This fascinated humans throughout the Second Republic. Even though most of the secrets have already been uncovered, Engineers still find study among the Ur-Obun to be interesting.

Councilors are often given a nice house in which to live. Nothing else is awarded them, except the good will of the people. They must accumulate riches through other means. Most Obun do not own land larger than a house and a garden, or a farm at the most. Some Councilors become land barons but they are usually disliked and their inheritance often reverts to the people upon their deaths.

Personages

Semana HanChantana

Known as one of the more successful diplomats during the Emperor Wars, Semana won the trust of many factions whom she parleyed with as a representative of the Church. While many called her a pawn for these parties, Semana persevered and was instrumental in the Sebastian-Dartmouth Treaty between the Hazat and the Hawkwood. As a side effect of that treaty, calling for a truce between the houses, their fiefs on Obun also halted hostilities. She is now in semiretirement, although she often leaves Obun to visit her cousin, Bran Botan voKarm, on Byzantium Secundus. Many suspect a plot between the two, and they are right. Semana and Botan are part of a secret cabal of councilors trying guide the Known Worlds towards a more peaceful path, one where divisions of hatred and suspicion between human and alien are dissolved.

Umo Nalu voDux

Nalu represents a new breed of Obun councilor: more cynical than his forebears. Tired of constant promises of equality from humans with little progress towards it, he is a true Doubting Thomas. His distrust of others has insulted certain human nobles on Obun, but he cares little for their feelings. Rather than waste his time in useless Council meetings, Nalu has taken to the stars, to find other aliens interested in building a strong coalition for alien rights. His experiences away from Obun have only made him more cynical and angry. He is now a loose cannon ready to go off at the slightest insult.

Roleplaying

Playing Ur-Obun

Suggested Stereotypes: Moral busybody (trying to improve the galaxy), concerned diplomat, peaceful plotter (trying to save the galaxy from itself), liberal hothead, conservative sage, mystic seer

Gamemastering

Following are some drama ideas involving Ur-Obun councilors:

· **The Activist:** Player characters become embroiled in a situation between a Muster slaver and an anti-slavery, Ur-Obun protester — actually a young councilor. The two nearly come to blows unless the characters can calm them down. Later, the Ur-Obun tries to enlist the characters aid in breaking into the slaver compound to free some slaves. If they do not aid him, he will label them moral cowards, and round up help from some less able but well meaning locals. Without the characters help, he and his motley gang will be caught by the slavers. For punishment they are shackled and shipped off-world as slaves to disappear on some distant world, their fate unknown. The characters find this out from one of the Obun's allies' friends, desperate for aid before the ship takes off that evening. What do they do? The Obun actually has allies in high positions among the Hawkwood, who will not appreciate hearing of the matter or of the character's laxity in the affair.

• **Portents:** The characters meet an old, diseased Ur-Obun living in an alien slum on some human world. If they are kind to him, he will invite them to his hovel, where he explains that he was once a famed orator on Obun. He came to this slum to save his fellows but got caught up in the poverty and despair. He will sing to himself and enter a deep trance. After a full minute where he is unresponsive to all stimuli, he will awaken and speak a true prophecy concerning the characters (he has the psychic power Omen). He will then leave to go beg in the streets, refusing all aid from the characters — he is done with them.

If they do not aid him upon first meeting, he will fall into a seizure and foretell some dire portent concerning

them — also true. This event will seem like a curse, haunting their steps; whether it actually comes to pass is up to the gamemaster. Regardless, the old Ur-Obun will continue on his way, contemptuous of any attempt by the characters to follow him.

Ur-Ukar

"Bring forward the traitor," Torquil oj Borduk said. "Let him stand trial before those he has betrayed." He looked to the al-Malik count sitting beside him and was pleased to see the smile on his face. He wants to see punishment. I will give him what he wants. The outlaw shall scream for mercy and I shall gain favor among the al-Malik.

The heavy stone doors of the throneroom opened to admit two heavy guards bearing an Ukar in chains. The wretch was half-naked and half-starved, obviously too weak to walk without aid. Torquil raised his hands and the guards stopped. With a gesture he bid them to release the captive. They moved aside, letting go their hold of his shoulders. The Ukar slumped but did not fall. Some inner reserve of dignity kept him up. In a few moments, he had straightened himself and stared at Torquil. A gaze of seething hatred.

Torquil looked to his guest. The al-Malik, Baron Iriman, looked disturbed but tried to hide it. What? Did the prisoner offend him? *Torquil snapped his fingers. "Come closer, criminal."*

"You are the criminal, son of Borduk," the captive said. "Your

forefathers sold our world to the human scum and you are their lap dog now. My only crime is killing those who would steal from rightful Ukari."

"Lies!" Torquil yelled. "Lies, Verlak Gant. You claim royal title even though such honor was stripped from your clan centuries ago. You led a rebellion against al-Malik householders in the Querto Dark, land which was rightfully given them by treaty well before you or I were born. How dare you question the wisdom of our forechiefs!"

"Land won through trickery and guile!" Verlak said, staring at Baron Iriman. "He knows it. Your 'guest' is well aware of how those caverns were taken for their mineral riches, their people displaced."

Baron Iriman coughed. Verlak had gone too far. Torquil looked to one of the guards. "Draw your sword and remove his head."

The guard looked at Torquil then at Verlak. He hesitated, and then stepped away, head bowed.

"What?!" Torquil sputtered. He looked to the other guard. "You! You do it."

The other guard likewise stepped away and would not meet his lord's eyes.

"I'll do it myself!" Torquil yelled, stepping down from the dais, drawing his sword. He approached Verlak and stared him in the eye. "I do this for the people of Ukar. You are condemned by their rightful ruler."

Verlak met his eye. "My chief, my rebellion is nothing to that which shall take place in your own soul."

The sword was raised and Verlak's head tumbled to the ground. Blood spurted across the room, spraying droplets on the fine silk gown of Baron Iriman. The baron grimaced and dabbed at the red stain. He rolled his eyes.

Torquil blacked out. For a few moments, he knew nothing. Then, his head cleared and he caught his balance. He looked about the room. Baron Iriman was hastily leaving and Torquil's own guardsmen stared at him in shock. And… was that admiration?

"What… what happened?" he said, weak.

The guards looked at each other. "My chief, you insulted the offworlder. Called him a murcha beast for causing you to execute a noble Ukari."

"I said what?!" Torquil cried. Then realization dawned on him. Verlak's curse had begun already. Torquil's execution of a man once loyal to him had awakened his laltach — his psychic Urge, which had possessed Torquil's mind and given voice to his true feelings, how deep down he hated the humans for what they made him do.

He stumbled back to his chair. Gods! That wasn't what he truly believed. He needed alliance with these offworlders, to cement his power. How could he ever apologize to the baron? How could humans begin to understand the dark, inner curse which haunted all Ukari?

Clan Wars

The Ukar have a clan society. The strongest bonds are formed with one's clan — with the strongest hatreds reserved for rival clans. However, since human subjugation,
traditional clan ties have grown weaker, creating an uprooted and alienated society. Among the many reasons for this was the dispersal of the clans, as the Church-led human occupation force broke up hostile clans, sending their members to various reservations throughout the Known Worlds — mainly on Aylon and Stigmata. But the main cause was the reversal of the traditional clan power structure, when the Church placed the weaker but human-friendly clans in power over the stronger but more hostile clans.

A handful of "traitor" clans — those who aided the humans against their rivals during the seige of Ukar — were given dominance over all other clans due to their ties with Known Worlders (mainly the League). Certain of the most hostile clans (those in charge of the Ukar War effort) were outlawed, their leaders sought as criminals and their lesser members sent to reservations away from the homeworld.

This has created a fractured society, where the traditional power elite now hide as outlawed freedom fighters, sabotaging League attempts to rape the resources of Ukar. Certain of these outlaw leaders, whose forefathers were once kings, are not even considered noble anymore, stripped long ago of their blood privilege. Their status is only recognized by fellow confederates and rebels.

Ukari Peerage

Clans are ruled from the top down by an Uluk (High Chieftain). His councilors and advisors are Dirgas (Chieftains), who each usually rule over a small village within the clan territory. Each village has a band of warriors, lead by a number of Braks. War parties or military units are lead by GoQuans, for they lead the Quans (Warriors). Most infantry, however, is made up of conscripted villagers, clan members without claim to noble title. Nobility is awarded through blood — the blood of chiefs — and through merit.

Long ago, before the Ukari reached the stars, the clans were forged into an empire of sorts by the legendary Darmak oj Malak, the first Grand Chieftain. This empire was quickly broken from within by sub-chiefs declaring themselves to be Grand Chieftains as well, creating a war of nations. This internal squabbling greatly aided the humans in the Ukar War, as rival factions sought human aid to overthrow the true Grand Chieftain. Now, the title is the equivalent of duke, or "one who holds many lands."

Today, Ukari nobles behave much the same as human nobles. Those from outlaw clans who still declare their royal, blood privilege titles must do so quietly, for it can be a capital offense. Many true Ukari nobles have been forced into exile offworld, to find their fortunes elsewhere, far from their traditional lands and family.

Rank Benefice

Ukari nobles now use the same terms as humans for their nobility. Sometimes these are translated to their traditional Ukari equivalents — the titles still used by outlaw nobility.

3 = Quan (Warrior, or Knight)

5 = GoQuan (First Warrior, or Baronet)

7 = Brak (Leader, or Baron)

9 = Dirga (Chieftain, or Earl)

11 = Uluk (High Chieftain, or Count)

13 = oj (literally "great scar": Grand Chieftain, or Duke; prefix added to family name)

Noble Scars

As with everything in Ukar society, a noble's status is revealed to others by his scars. Elaborate glyphs represent not only the noble's clan but his rank within that clan. Traditionally, such scars are carved on the forehead, but the outlaw clans must carve theirs in hidden places (armpit, lower back, inner thigh, etc.)

Holdings

The quisling clans were given what the humans considered to be the prime lands: those on the hostile surface of the planet, closest to the human-constructed atmosphere domes and spaceports. The irony of this is that these lands were traditionally considered the slums, not far from these clans' own lands just below the surface. Humans could not understand that, in the Ukari subterranean culture, the most prized lands were those farthest from the surface, in the darkest, most noxious regions on the planet's bowels.

Thus, by the strange reversal, the outlaw clans still hold their traditional fiefs, those now ignored and even feared by the human occupiers. In these now discarded regions, the atmosphere technology which once kept the cavern estates livable is now running down, making many of these fiefs dangerous, gaseous slums.

Subsistence

Many Ukari now work for the humans in the surface domed cities, aiding the League to extract mineral wealth from the planet. Those who still live underground are usually the poorest of the Ukar, reduced to ancient methods of hunting and horticulture to survive. Like their ancestors, many underground dwellers work on fungus farms, or aid in the preparation of "paste", a nutritious but tasteless food staple made with synthetic technologies (imported spices are popular among those whose main diet consists of paste). Such harvests are supplemented with occasional hunts: bugs, giant voles, unique mammals and undersea fishes.

Personages

Torquil oj Borduk

As the ruler of all Ukari, Torquil constantly walks a razor's edge between the needs of his people and the need to appease Known World outsiders interfering with Ukari business. Since the Merchant League nominally "owns" the homeworld, Torquil must constantly fight off their attempts to do what they will with the planet, while still

maintaining their respect. If the Leaguemeister were to decide that Torquil was not friendly enough to the League, then he would support another clan leader instead, and Torquil's power would be greatly diminished. In addition, Torquil must look out for the needs of Ukari in reservations on Aylon. (Those who were on Stigmata are lost.)

Torquil's worst enemy, however, is his own soul. A powerful psychic trained in the path of Psyche, Torquil's Urge is strong. Too many conflicting duties have only increased the rift between his self and his inner twin. He fears the day it will gain complete control of him, and knows that he really should retreat on a religious pilgrimage to conquer it. But to do so would remove him from power for too long, and risk another, more toadying Ukar chief, gaining power.

Dirga Zozos Feldak

As both a chieftain of an outlaw clan and a priest of Banjak, the traditional, native Ukari religion, Zozos is doubly damned in the eyes of the human authorities. While the League could really care less as long as he stays out of sight and does nothing against their interests, the Avestite busybodies are greatly offended at such a figure as Zozos, seeing in him a true threat. But Zozos only wants to be left alone by outsiders. He has enough trouble leading his poor people in their life deep in the Ukar caverns, far from the humans and recognized clans. Indeed, many Ukari are unaware that his clan still exists, so little mark do they make on surface world life. But many offworlders come to Ukar to search the deep caverns and tunnels for Ur artifacts; these meddlers often have to reckon with Zozos, and he is most unkind to such intruders.

Roleplaying

Playing Ur-Ukar

Suggested Stereotypes: Quisling (licking the boots of the occupation forces), outlaw (resisting human imposed rule), decadent lord (party down while you can, it's all going to hell), honorable noble (holding to old values of honor and loyalty — to those who deserve it), cosmic-plotter (allying with occultists and others to overturn human rule).

Gamemastering

· **Terror on the Achilles:** The characters are taking passage aboard the luxury liner Achilles (they are either working their way for passage or have been hired by a noble to escort someone on the voyage). All goes well on the way to the jumpgate, but once the ship exits into its destination system, the ship is taken over by Ur-Ukar terrorists. They demand the release of fellow clan members being held on the destination planet and will kill everyone on board if their fellows are not delivered to the Achilles within a week. Their leader is an outlaw clan noble.

The real problem is that the local authorities (choose a noble house) do not want to release the criminals, and

there is no one important enough to them on board to make it worth their while. Despite the protestations of the Church, they're willing to call the terrorists' bluff. What can the characters do to either change their minds or defuse the situation? If pressed, the Ur-Ukari will actually only kill human nobles from the house refusing to deal with them. They will then force everyone into cramped lifeboats and steal the liner, abandoning it on the other side of their jump (where pirate allies await to sneak them away).

Traits

Background Affliction

Outlaw Clan Title (3 pts): The character's noble status (he must buy noble rank separately) is only recognized by outlaw clans. To these clans, he may be a hero, holding to his traditional rank against all censure, but to the recognized Ukari and human authorities, he is a criminal.

Vorox

"Greetings, my lord," Sir Huang Xu Li Halan said, trying not to reveal his disgust at the duke's stench by bowing slightly at the waist in deference to the noble. "How was your journey?"

"Cramped," the duke muttered, stretching his four arms out — a span almost as wide as Huang Xu was tall. The Li Halan started, but told himself that this was not a hostile gesture, no matter what it looked like. These lumoxes don't know to behave properly, he thought. Patience.

The duke continued: "Your starships are not built for one of my great size. Pity. Perhaps your lord will gift me one built to size…"

Not likely, thought Huang Xu. Waste such effort on an uncivilized beast who would know not what to do with it if he had it? No, that won't happen anytime soon. But he hid his contemplations from the giant Vorox with a smile. "I shall take you to him immediately."

"Good," the duke said, bending down to look Huang Xu in the eye. "I've been waiting too long already." He reached out with one huge hand and carefully unfurled a single claw, which he used to tap against Huang Xu's brooch. "My, that's a pretty bauble. I'd like one like that. We primitives do like shiny things, no?"

Huang Xu broke a sweat. He could see the slight purplish stain at the end of the claw, a sign of the poison which coated it. "Uh… Most humorous, my lord. It is said that Vorox senses are keen indeed."

Duke Glom smiled. "I'm glad you agree." He withdrew the clawed hand and motioned down the hall. "After you…"

Civilizing the Savages

The Second Republic anthropologists who first ushered the sentient Vorox into Known Worlds life did so slowly and carefully. After the initial fear of these creatures abated, their better qualities were noticed. The anthropologists devised a regimen of training for Vorox which would allow them to recognize human social cues

and surpress their instincts. Eventually, certain Vorox were allowed to roam freely among Known Worlds society, having proven their ability to discern reason from instinct.

After the Fall, the Li Halan took over the task of civilizing the Vorox, and they drew the line between civilized and feral, a division previous anthropologists had been loathe to make, even though it seemed that some Vorox refused to submit to the repression involved in the civilizing process. The Li Halan also refused to recognize the nascent Vorox culture as worthy, and instead tried to impose their own idea of what a Vorox culture should be. The result is actually a mix of the two ideals.

The early Li Halan sought the Vorox as shock troops for their decadent wars and pleasures. Later Li Halan, after the house's conversion, sought to make the Vorox model citizens, humble before the Pancreator.

Nonetheless, following the lead of their forefathers, they emphasized a noble class, even though there had been none as such among the Vorox before the Fall. The Li Halan chose those who best represented their civilizing efforts (in their opinions) and set them up as a royal family, claiming that they were descended from the first civilized Vorox. Of course, no proof of bloodlines existed in the culture, more concerned with pack ties than blood, but the lie was eventually accepted — by the civilized if not by the feral.

Thus, Vorox nobility forms a class removed from natural Vorox culture. While nobles have been well adapted into Vorox social structures, the fact that they are still alien can be seen in the hatred reserved for them by ferals. Indeed, the fact that they are allowed to keep one of their deadly claws effectively removes the pretense of equality.

Most Vorox nobles are found only on their homeworld; few roam the stars. However, there are exceptions, especially among those who lands are threatened by ferals — the best remedy is usually to leave for a while until the fighting dies down. This is not cowardice, as the Li Halan say, simply prudence.

Li Halan are often accused of deliberately keeping Vorox ignorant and naive of Known Worlds political realities. But the pious nobles claim that they only seek to protect Vorox from themselves and others.

The Angerak

Vorox have a strong pack instinct; at the core of their society is the angerak, or the pack. Packs vary in size depending on region and need; some are as small as three while others can extend to nearly 50 Vorox.

Each angerak has a leader and a loose hierarchy under him or her; every Vorox has a place in this chain, even if it is mobile and everchanging. The ties a Vorox has to his or her angerak siblings are stronger than any known blood ties among humans. Family is not a strong enough word to encompass the emotion and bonding between angerak members. While some members of the angerak may be blood relatives, such ties are unimportant to the greater link of the pack. "The angerak is one soul, one blood."

There is a powerful ritual for initiating someone into the angerak. Among ferals, this is a long, drawn out dance of sorts. Among the civilized Vorox, it has been greatly influenced by the Church and is now more litany than physical trial, but it is still effective nonetheless.

Non-Vorox may be admitted to an angerak. Vorox who are far from home and their own kind go mad without such a bond, and will usually seek out others to form an angerak, even if its only temporary. While civilized Vorox can sometimes sever their bonds to an angerak, feral find it very hard to do so, for their instincts rule their choices. Even the civilized may go through a period of deep depression, even if the severing was voluntary.

Nobles are automatically considered the leaders of their own angerak, and the estate of the nobility is considered a more abstract form of an angerak, sort of an uberpack bonding all civilized packs. It does not hold the emotional power a real angerak does, but it is heeded. There is one Vorox placed above all others, a king meant to unify Vorox civilization (according to Li Halan thinking, at least). There have been good kings and bad kings, but the role's success has depended more on goodwill with the Li Halan than with the Vorox.

The rank of a noble is determined by the size of his angerak; the larger the pack, the greater the rank. In addition, territory is important. Large or rich territory may allow a Vorox to claim a greater title than his angerak would normally allow. Vorox use human terms for nobility (knight, baron, etc.). These positions were once more fluid than today, but with the marking of permanent territory, the titles have become hereditary for the angerak rulers.

When a noble dies, a member of his angerak replaces him, chosen from birth to be an heir and thus retain a claw. This does not have to be a blood relative — again, the pack bond supersedes blood bonds. Often, many young Vorox are chosen and given an heir order, in case one dies before assuming the title. Thus, like human nobles, Vorox have second and third "sons" and "daughters" who may never inherit any real power.

The Declawing

Part of the civilizing process involves enforced declawing. No human wants a Vorox running around the Known Worlds with poison claws. They are nervous enough about letting the nobles do it, but since it was a tradition begun by the early, pre-conversion Li Halan, it is hard to change it now. So far, there have been few tragedies as a result.

The declawing is a rather traumatic event which is only healed with the help of the Vorox's angerak siblings. Over time, the Vorox have discovered methods of dealing with it which leave few psychic scars. The best method is the derogation of ferals; by painting their feral cousins as uncouth savages, they rise above them. Because of the repression involved in the civilizing process, many civilized Vorox project their pain and hurt onto the ferals, who likewise hate the civilized Vorox for what they have done to the homeworld (giving much of it away to offworld interests).

Holdings

Each angerak has a territory. For ferals, this region varies as they move about in a semi-nomadic life. For civilized, the territories are mapped and set in stone, much as with humans and their fiefs. The leader of the angerak is the ruler of the fief, and he thus owns all the product of his angerak's labor on that fief.

All Vorox lands are administered by Li Halan. While

the lands actually belong to the Vorox by title, a long history of pacts and treaties with the Li Halan in return for material and political assistance has given much of their wealth to the offworld house. Most Vorox are not even aware of this.

Personages

Kummanga

The ruler of all Vorox, Kummanga is renowned as one of the better kings in history — to the Vorox, at least. The Li Halan have grown to dislike him, for he seems all too canny about human politics, and is thus less manipulable. He knows this and actually hides the true extent of his lore from them. He is in fact a master politician and has made secret allies with the al-Malik and many minor houses, and with certain high-ranking members of the League. He hopes to one day remove Li Halan control of his world, although he knows that one human faction or another will replace them. He wants to be the one to choose that faction.

He is a powerful Vorox even by that race's standards. He gained much renown fighting feral discontents before his angerak father passed away, leaving the kingship to him.

KagongKagong

A feral Vorox, KagongKagong has lead many of his fellow ferals against civilized fiefs, looting and destroying what they could and fleeing again to the trackless jungles. His angerak knows the unmapped wildernesses better than any civilized Vorox could ever hope to, and they use this to good tactical advantage. The Li Halan have even tried to intervene and make treaty with him, but he ate their emissaries and sent their bones back on a string. In retaliation, the horrified Li Halan have placed a sizable bounty on his head which has sent many unwitting human bounty hunters into the jungle. The ferocious predators of the planet have usually disposed of the intruders well before they can even come near KagongKagong or his angerak. For now, his rebellion continues.

Roleplaying

Vorox Characters

Suggested Stereotypes: Noble savage, reluctant prince (doesn't want the responsibility or wants to run free in the jungle), despot (has taken the worst examples of human rule as her guide), indecisive king (civilization brings too many decisions — which one is the right one?), incog-nito king (trying to learn among those who will not treat him as a noble), savage king ("By this axe I rule")

Gamemastering Vorox

Unlike human nobles, Vorox have a harder time breaking off from their homes and traveling footloose and fancy free with but an entourage behind them. Their very title is tied to their pack and lands; without those, they would not truly be noble, even though they might be allowed to claim the title.

Most Vorox nobles encountered off the homeworld will have a purpose and reason for being away from their lands, whether it be a diplomatic mission, a war party or simply a vacation.

Player character nobles should have a good reason for being away from home (avoiding rivals, on a mission for the Li Halan, in exile, etc.) and should induct long-term traveling companions into their angerak. This can get tricky, because technically, the noble rules the entire angerak, and thus any other player character admitted to it. However, exceptions are often made for human rank and title; the Vorox sometimes recognize a League or Church title as highly as noble rank. Such characters may be considered equals — sometimes.

Here are some drama ideas involving Vorox nobles:

· **Visiting Dignitary:** The player characters must play host to a visiting noble: a Vorox baron, newly civilized and still uncouth. But it is an insult to reveal this to him, so the characters have to pretend that he is acting perfectly normal. Only another noble can be so privileged as to reveal his *faux pas* to him.

· **The Savage Land:** A renegade Vorox has taken his entire angerak and seized a human fief. The player characters must either parley with him or they have accidentally wandered onto his lands and are captured. Can they talk their way out of this? Catering to his royal ego will help, but treating him like a savage will raise his ire.

Traits

Graa (Vorox Martial Art) Action

Shang ("Dire Claw," Level 5): This action can only be learned by noble Vorox, those who still have a single, natural claw. This action trains the noble to deliver a powerful, slashing strike with that dreaded symbol of his rank.

Roll	Init	Goal	DMG	Effect
Dx+Fight	-1	—	4	If at least one point of damage penetrates the victim's armor, then poison takes effect

Ur-Obun Ruling Council

Ur-Ukar Chiefdom

Vorox Kingdom